D1591468

THE BIRDS OF DOG

The Birds of Dog

AN HISTORICAL NOVEL
BASED ON MOSTLY TRUE EVENTS

Ann B. Parson

LUMINARE PRESS
WWW.LUMINAREPRESS.COM

The Birds of Dog: An Historical Novel Based on Mostly True Events
Copyright © 2023 by Ann B. Parson

All rights reserved. This book or any portion thereof may not be reproduced or used in any manner whatsoever without the express written permission of the publisher, except for the use of brief quotations in a book review.

Printed in the United States of America

Luminare Press
442 Charnelton St.
Eugene, OR 97401
www.luminarepress.com

LCCN: 2023914799
ISBN: 979-8-88679-274-4

With Sandy Hook in mind,
And the centuries-old slaughter of wildlife never forgotten.

Dedicated to George A. Parson, John D. Parson
and Stephen P. Parson

Boston circa 1838. Courtesy of Stokes Collection, New York Public Library

Note: While the narrator, Catharine, and a few others spring from the imagination, most of this account is based on real people and true events. The book's many stories, retold in the author's own words, come from diverse sources, each publication cited in the endnotes. Direct quotes are from:

"Hunting Without A Gun" by Rowland Robinson (p. 42)

"Notes on the Peeping Frog" by Mary Hinkley (p. 137)

"Sixty Years Ago" by Harriet Hemenway (p. 176)

Letters and journals by Charles Pickering

Credit: Boston Athenaeum for reproductions of *Coasting in the Common, Boston Athenaeum on Pearl Street* and *Cutting's and Butler's Grand Aquaria.* Credit: Digital Commonwealth, *Common American Swan.*

Contents

Coasting in The Common, 1856, from Ballou's Pictorial

Preface

WINTER, 1895

Sophie my little bear, my grandchild,

When winter arrived early this year, and the shouts of children sledding down the Common's long diagonal rose up like the whoop of Indians, I thought of Catharine, and how she relished a good, blustery snowstorm. Snowflakes pecking on windowpanes; snow crunching underfoot; the swoosh of snow sliding off the roof.

"Let's go outside and hear the snow voice," she'd say.

The other night, filled with memories, I retrieved the bundle of letters from the drawer where Cath left them, poured a dark whiskey and fell back in time. Written to a cousin she adored, Charles Pickering, the correspondence spans four years, from 1838 to 1842, when Charles was off circling the globe. Had any of her originals gone astray, and some likely did, Cath had painstakingly copied each one. The duplicates, tied together with a red ribbon, would be there waiting for Charles upon his return, even though Cath would not.

Cath died twenty-five years before the typewriter appeared, an invention that led to carbon paper's popularity. Inventions are like that. They seem to come in twos and threes.

Carbon paper certainly would have made her life easier.

For you, Sophie, I'll fill in as much about those curious times as my wobbly old head can recall. First this. Boston in those days was showing itself to be the cradle for America's nascent sciences—far more than Philadelphia, in my opinion—and its wide-eyed naturalists were obsessed with collecting and cataloguing every bird and bug they came across.[1] So obsessed, I'm afraid, that they didn't think twice about the heavy-handedness of their actions. Catharine wouldn't at first understand what she was witnessing, or why it bothered her so much. But as you'll see, she wouldn't only come to terms with her apprehensions, she'd try to put the evil spirits back in the box.

The Navy had recruited Charles as chief zoologist for a major ocean expedition—the country's first voyage of discovery to the South Seas—so you can imagine the pride and excitement our family felt when the U.S. Exploring Expedition left the Virginian coast in August 1838. Its six ships had 346 men onboard, nine of whom were Scientifics. That is, gentlemen of science in contrast to military scientists. Their assignment was to send home natural specimens from every ocean, every distant land. Charles was by far the most knowledgeable. He may have been of meager build and modest nature, but, much like his grandfather, Col. Timothy, he was high-energy. An overachiever. While the other Scientifics could claim one or two areas of expertise, Charles had a firm grasp of several—among them, entomology, ornithology, ichthyology, and conchology. As another zoologist put it, our cousin combined a dozen disciplines in one small body.

Later, studying the human races of several continents, Charles lifted up another corner of science. Some today consider him America's first anthropologist of serious merit. He had an interesting theory, that all humans had originated in Africa. But back then, proof was slim.

His love of nature began early. After her husband died of throat cancer, his mother Lurena left rural Pennsylvania, she and her two sons eventually settling in with the boys' grandparents, Rebecca and the Colonel, at the old Pickering homestead in Salem. The original crude saltbox was built in 1651 by a forefather with remarkably clever hands—the "mechanical ability," people called it in those days—a trait passed down to more than a few carpenters and instrument wielding scientists in our family.[2] (Consider cousin Edward, who directs Harvard College Observatory, and who years ago, let's not forget, designed an early speaking tube but chose not to patent it, because of his belief that scientific information should be free for the asking. And his brother, William, also a physicist, who studies the moon and the stars.)

Butterflies, starfish, beetles or speckled lizards. Whatever caught Charles' fancy he brought home to poke and study, making sure to draw their likenesses in his red-leather sketchbook, *Charles' catalogus insectorium*. His drawings were so meticulous and lifelike, they brought him early recognition as an entomologist, an authority on bugs. During his student years at Harvard College, then medical school, his excursions into the White Mountains with the botanist William Oakes rounded Charles into a full-fledged naturalist. It's said that no others knew New England's trees and plants better than those two. Charles practiced medicine, but briefly. Natural history was turning into a legitimate profession, and without much trouble he found work as a curator at Philadelphia's Academy of Natural Sciences, the country's foremost collection of natural artifacts. The Academy was a perfect place for Charles, whose knowledge of species was already so voluminous, his co-workers consulted him like "a dictionary," the botanist Asa Gray later recounted about your hard-working cousin.

When asked to join the U.S. Exploring Expedition, Charles must have leapt at the chance. He was single and his employment on dry land could be deferred. While his own father wasn't around to cheer him on, his uncles John and Octavius did, and with bullish enthusiasm. At first, the natural treasures the explorers shipped home were to go to any institution that wanted them. Later, the best and most rare were kept at the nation's capital, where eventually they formed the beginning nest of objects displayed at the new national museum, the Smithsonian Institution. What many people still don't realize is that our Charles was the very first curator of that trove.

The fleet met up with such horrid weather, there must have been times when our small, wiry cousin was nearly blown overboard. Not that he stayed trouble-free. On islands and the wild mainland, he was cornered by animals and natives, but effectively worked his way out of these jams. He sprang his ankle and his glasses got smashed. Yet, he was an organized sort and had packed bandages, salves and even extra lenses.

Regrettably, the U.S. Exploring Expedition—also known as the "Wilkes" voyage after its commander Charles Wilkes—is nearly forgotten, when the

H.M.S. *Beagle*'s earlier voyage, a smaller affair out of England with Charles Darwin on board, is stitched into time. It turned out that the Wilkes fleet was the last major voyage to circumnavigate the globe under sail. "Our machineries are sending us backward," my father often complained, a born contrarian, and I've come to agree with him. New technologies have had devastating effects on the natural world. Humans might feel improved, but on the whole, our advances often come at the expense of plants and animals, the soil, the ocean, air and sky, all the entities we depend upon.

So much went wrong during the Expedition that Father and other grumblers took to calling it "Wilkes's Deplorable Expedition." Still, in those days, a boat was little more than a wooden scrap adrift on an impulsive sea, and many Bostonians, including Charles' uncles, John and Octavius, commended Capt. Wilkes for his bold leadership. He had anticipated losing two ships, and, as it turned out, two did go down. But only the crew of one ship perished, and thankfully our cousin wasn't among them.

You'll find that Catharine often includes a "Troc'ulus" or two in her letters, which needs some explanation. A distant Pickering ancestor used to tell his grandchildren a fanciful story about a Troc'ulus, a type of chimney swallow now rarely seen. It happened that in Colonial days, when a flock of these birds left a chimney they had inhabited, they dropped one of their young down to the people below, a gift of sorts. To Catharine and Charles, any interesting tale taken from Nature was a gift fitting to be dropped down the chute. So they made a game out of it. You find a Troc'ulus for me, and I'll find one for you.

A Troc'ulus for a Troc'ulus. A story for a story.

USS Vincennes in Disappointment Bay, Antarctica 1840. Line engraving by C.A. Jewett, after a sketch by Charles Wilkes. Source: Navy Historical Center

Boston Athenaeum on Pearl Street, first home of the
Boston Society of Natural History, about 1830 [3]

PART 1

The Nonconformist
and The Zoologist

To Charles Pickering aboard the USS Vincennes
From Catharine Pickering, Boston
September 5, 1838

Dearest Charles,

   The *Vincennes* sailed from Hampton roads only last week, but it feels like a century ago. I hate the idea of your being so far away, for so long. Whom can I take to concerts? Who will whisper and laugh with me at Algonquin lectures? By the time this letter reaches you, if it ever does, you'll be somewhere off the coast of South America encountering alien natives and observing strange twists of Nature. Oh, my nonstop imagination! I keep seeing you in your netted mosquito hat wading through a leafy jungle teeming with monkeys, big birds and orange insects. These daydreams, I'm finding, are a perfect escape from the dull chatter of Mrs. Macomber and her sewing group, not to mention Reverend Broadlawn's tedious sermons. If there is a God, our preacher is letting him down. On Sunday, half the congregation fell sleep, the rumble of snores quite humorous.

I wish you had a small viewing box that could return every detail of your surroundings back to us, as fast as a star racing across the night sky. Father says such an invention is certain to happen, but not anytime soon.

Here, the warmth of summer lingers. I fly out at every chance knowing winter will soon pull a different sky over our heads. Just yesterday Mother and I took a leisurely stroll on ground destined for the new Public Garden, then went around the corner to the old circus building that Mr. Gray is turning into a Conservatory.[4] He plans to fill it with exotic birds and plants, which Father isn't thrilled about given its proximity to our own Beacon Street roost.[5] There isn't much to see yet, save for a caged ostrich and two curassows who wander freely about. Their head curls bring Socrates to mind.[6]

Why do humans think they own the earth, when here is a bird whose ancestry goes back twenty-five million years!

An attendant told us there's a plan afoot in the farming community for curassows to replace chickens in poultry yards. They are easier to tame, and their meat is more delicate. I wanted to ask him, isn't it possible to raise these noble looking creatures for no reason at all? Certainly not to kill them? But since none of this is the attendant's fault, I stayed quiet.

You made Mary and me promise to regularly share our news, so each month I'll keep a letter open, as if you're right here and I can talk to you on a whim.

In the brief time you've been gone, at least no more sadness has rocked the family. The loss of Dr. Bowditch in March followed by Uncle Henry's sudden illness has turned Father's hair nearly white. It's still hard for him to fathom that both his brother and best boyhood friend are gone. No one understands Nat Bowditch's mind for mathematics better, and requests for Father to speak about his friend are constantly dropped through the mail slot. At a recent dinner at the Howes, Father recounted how, when they were boys, Dr. Bowditch solved a problem so fast, his teacher sent him to the headmaster's office for cheating. "Too bad that teacher isn't alive today," Father mentioned. "Due to Nat's grasp of longitude, my nephew's passage to the Southern Ocean will be hugely safer. And ships everywhere enjoy a new freedom."

Father also mentioned the camera lucida you have on board, and how it will help your artists draw everything from animals to mountains. The Boston Society of Natural History plans to demonstrate this new device, and I plan to be there.

Which leads me to this news. I'm curious about what goes on at the Society, and wrote to Dr. Binney to see if I could volunteer. According to Uncle Octavius, a staggering number of objects come through the door—recently two Mammoth tusks!—and they are terribly shorthanded.[7] Since both Uncle O. and Father are active supporters, perhaps I stand a chance. I'd be given the dullest of jobs—I'm a woman, after all. But never mind. I could send you the Society's news. And for our game of trading stories from Nature, I'd have an entire library to rummage around in.

There's some small progress at the Society. Women can now attend social gatherings. It surprises the members—the men, that is—that attendance at evening lectures has shot way up. "Why does a woman want to bother her pretty head with particulars about this or that specimen?" I overheard Mr. Winthrop say this to Mr. Vernon at the last event.

"Pretty is as pretty does," I thought to myself.

How much longer, I wonder, before women achieve full membership? How much longer, for that matter, until women pervade every corner of the sciences? I'm afraid I'll be bone dust by then!

Sliding toward insurrection. That's how I think of myself these days. Favorite cousin, you know I'm not the coiffed, flirtatious sort who goes out of her way to attract a suitor. I have little interest in the latest fashions, and I'm not overly concerned if my hair is mussed or my underskirts dragging. Nodding sweetly to gentlemen acquaintances passing on the street isn't in my nature, and sometimes their invitations lay forgotten on my desk & Mother gets very upset. Last week I forgot to reply to Wadsworth Cabot, Boston's "most eligible," Mrs. Macomber would have you believe. By which she means, rich and powerful.

"Why haven't you answered him?" Mother wailed. "I don't understand you, Catharine!"

Too much honesty has a way of tumbling out of me. "Mr. Cabot reminds me of a crab—those protruding eyes and waving claws. Honestly, a crab on the beach is more my type!" What I didn't say about Mr. Cabot is that his preoccupation with hunting bothers me very much, and while many men do it, Mr. Cabot's eagerness to kill seems particularly tied to a mean spirit. His parlor's dozens of glassy-eyed trophies—I wanted to run out the door the time I visited.

Poor Mother. Her face was pale, her eyes confused. She can't hide her disappointment that both daughters have no prospects in sight. That we might end up "husband-less." "What will become of you, Catharine?" she asked, drooping with despair.

That's when I sat down and wrote Dr. Binney. For surely, marriage is only one of several options.

September 15, 1838

Here's a Troc'ulus, saved from last Monday's *Atlas*.[8] The spider at its center lives in a pork house down by the wharves, where its activities drew onlookers day after day.

For as long as a week, the spider built a two-foot-high web that had an exceptionally thick and sturdy base, and one day a mouse wandered into it. The spider, working quickly, kept spinning around the mouse, until neither its legs nor tail touched the floor. The more the mouse tried to free himself, the more his entire body became ensnared. Satisfied his victim was going nowhere, the spider began eating the mouse's ear, just as if the mouse were a big fly. The ear began to bleed profusely. Word of the slow torture brought more and more onlookers. How long would it take the spider to devour its victim? "Five weeks!" someone guessed. "Five months!" someone else exclaimed.

Finally, one spectator couldn't stand the sight any longer. Having more sympathy for the mouse than curiosity for the slow death it was undergoing, he liberated "the miserable quadruped from the merciless fangs of his insect enemy," the *Atlas* reported. The crowd dispersed, and that was that, thank heavens.

Remember the excitement before you left—the opening of the Eastern Railroad connecting Boston to towns to the north? Mother, Father, and I rode the rail to Salem this past Sunday and found it smooth, rapid, and scenic. Off in the distance we spotted deer, fox, and even bear. One black bear was up on his hind legs staring after us, and I wondered what he was thinking of this clattering, deafening object speeding through his serene landscape.

As for the other new rail, the Providence line that crosses the Bay below us. Apparently, errors were made when its tracks were put down. Trains arriving and departing shake and rattle so, passengers are frequently tossed from their seats. Mr. Sutcliffe was tossed so hard last week, he broke his nose. Father refers to such early mistakes as "growing pains." Despite them, he expects railroad usage will soar, and quickly.

September 20, 1838

A returning captain brought word that the Wilkes' fleet has reached Madeira. Our hoots filled the kitchen. What relief to know your ship rode out last week's storm without mishap.

Now, if only a bird could fly this letter straight to the Vincennes. Carried by boat, my news will be antediluvian by the time it reaches you.

Dr. Binney sent a note saying that the directors of the Natural History Society would welcome my help twice a week with cataloguing, labeling, dusting the cabinet and procuring books for the library. I'm ecstatic! It leaves time for tutoring Abigail Warburton and that little hellion, our cousin Oliver. (His latest fun has been to drop worms on people's heads from the attic window, and yesterday the fishman slipped on one and threatened to stop his deliveries.) Just yesterday I actually met with Dr. Binney. His posture is so erect, his manner so formal, on past occasions I mistook him as arrogant. But this time I found him to be the opposite, cordial and self-effacing. And his passion for natural objects—he refers to them as "beautiful manifestations of divine wisdom"—is every bit as fierce as yours.

He's alarmed at how quickly the Society's new quarters above the Savings Bank on Tremont Street are filling. The rooms are commodious, with tall windows delivering a grand view of The Common, and yet the curators are already running out of display space and must store objects in drawers out of view. A large delivery of invertebrates from the Aegean just about swamped the staff. So Dr. Binney has implemented a change in policy. The founders' rule, that Boston captains bring back objects from every sea and every continent, no longer applies. Now the curators will primarily collect plants, birds, and fish from local regions; and only occasional rarities from distant shores.

"We must resist the temptation to collect everything under the sun," said Dr. Binney. Cousin, you and the other Scientifics must battle this temptation every day!

Dr. Binney's own fossils, minerals, and mounted birds—the nucleus that began the collection—are elegantly displayed. As are Capt. Couthouy's 800 species of shells. Tell the Captain his treasures reside in a new case made by the New England Glass Company, the same skillful glassblowers who made the jars holding our fish and reptiles.[9] Our Cabinet Keeper, Mr. Hamilton, says we are catching up to Philadelphia's older collection. We can claim over 14,000 specimens of insects, one of the largest collections of its kind. And we also house every known species of Massachusetts reptile, with one exception. Not to leave out 90 of the state's 120 species of fish.[10]

Can anyone know precisely how many fish types exist within State waters? I asked Dr. Binney this, and he vaguely explained it has to do with fish counts each week. (I guess I ask too many questions. But Father's right; you learn lots when you play dumb.) The bird cabinet is also growing rapidly. Its curator, Jeremy Winkler, seems more honest when he says no one knows for sure which species are common to Massachusetts.[11]

Dr. Binney feels we're still in the dark ages. "Not one catalogue! Nothing of a general history of the State's animals has existed up until now. We have a long way to go before we know other creatures half as well as we know ourselves."

And that's a pittance.

September 21, 1838

The best part of my job? Without a doubt the naturalists and the treasures they drop off. Edward Tuckerman & his esteem for the lowly lichens that grip stone, dead wood, animal bone as no other life forms can or do. And Walter Wellington, the tall wisp of a gentleman from New Bedford who collects butterflies. And Junie Eaton, the stuttering Mainer who deposits an occasional bear hide and string of claws.

The staff's favorite botanist appears to be Thomas Nuttall. So many species named in his honor—I had no idea! Nuttall's woodpecker, Nuttall's scrub oak, Nuttall's violet, Nuttall's snapdragon, and on the list goes. Your friend Mr. Audubon recently named a nocturnal bird from the west "Nuttall's whip-poor-will."[12]

"*Whip poor will!* The bird sings those three notes. *Whip poor will!*"

Quite frankly, I'm not sure what to make of young Henry Thoreau, fresh out of College. He comes in regularly with bird nests, insects pinned to bark, reptile skins, and arrowheads, too. Many! He has a knack for finding them. He's a bit of a strange breed, don't you think? Those sunken eyes and uncomely nose. And that grizzly neckbeard. Poor man, he's as ugly as a crocodile, and yet as sharp-eyed as a harrier. He asked me to accompany him out to the harbor islands to look for objects, and though I'm half inclined, I wish you were here to join us.

His comments and beliefs give me a lot to think about. Unlike the other naturalists, he hardly ever donates a dead animal. "I don't like killing things," he told me. "A man who kills a creature must be dead himself to take the life of an innocent. And that's why I despise the contents of museums, there's so much deadness everywhere. Dead animals collected by dead men!"[13]

Our collection offends him less than some, he said, since it invites "contemplation and not just gawping." What profound honesty comes from this strange man.

When parents bring their children—a good excuse for their own visit, I suspect—the children skip about until something catches their eye and they fasten to a case like suction cups. Is that what Henry Thoreau means by "gawping?" Mr. Greenwood's establishment down the street, with its oddities and art objects, is a magnet for gawpers. We were disappointed lately when Vice President Johnson, who was in town for a convention, strode by our door on his way to that more flamboyant collection. Does that mean our President is a gawper?

Mary and I attended the Society's demonstration of the camera lucida last night and we're still talking about the instrument this morning. It perfectly replicated a member's profile—the likeness was probably truer than Mrs. Gould would have liked, since it magnified her several chins—and also made such a clear image of books on a shelf, each title was distinct and readable. Mr. Peale and the voyage's other artists must be delighted with this device.

Yet I wonder. Using it, are they still artists? The drawing arm has so little to do now, the imagination even less.

WINTER, 1895

Sophie bear, here's a bit more history before it sinks beyond reach.

Catharine began volunteering at the Boston Society of Natural History in the fall of 1838, eight years after its founding. The organization's all-male circle seems not to have intimidated her, not in the least. Her dependable care of the collections earned her the curators' utmost respect. Even Peter Wick, who was forever swiping his finger over surfaces, found no dust motes to grumble about.

Of course, it didn't go unnoticed, in an all-male circle, how pretty Catharine was, this shapely young woman with lucid brown eyes and wavy chestnut hair. Her smile could easily light up a room. And the way she laughed—it could strip the doom off gloomy old men and make creaky old matrons spry again. She dressed with an eye to the weather, comfort and health, rather than fashion, and yet whatever she wore suited her. Once, at Adelaide Frothingham's Christmas party, Adelaide was dressed in pale silk, a stunning Kashmir over her shoulders, and yet Cath, wearing a plain red frock, was the party's exquisite wild rose.

Like her father, John the linguist, and her sister Mary, an adept writer and editor, Cath had a hungry mind and consumed books like sweets. She was endowed with the Pickering energy—as well as the family's bent nose, I might add. Her father, John Pickering, was proficient in twenty-two languages, including Egyptian hieroglyphics. Twenty-two! Her cousin Charles, overflowing with the same energy, was such a rigorous examiner of Nature that the books he wrote, I'm sorry to say, are unreadable mountains. The Swiss naturalist Louis Agassiz once confessed that Charles' history of plants, which stretches to over 1000 pages, gave him "a giant headache."

At the Society, Cath did the work of at least two assistants. Indispensable straight up until she fell ill, she kept the clocks wound, the orchids watered, the newspapers neat. All those tasks that tend to go unnoticed and yet are missed when left undone.

Other museums in our city were filling with natural riches, but what set the Boston Society of Natural History apart was its curators' strict adherence to scientific methods. A studious approach to objects was catching on, practiced by a widening circle of scientists whose curiosity about life drove them to explore deeper and deeper. The Society, in fact, was the first in New England to look at specimens through the lens of the sciences, and it eventually became a world leader, second only in this country to the Academy of Natural Sciences in Philadelphia.[14]

September 24, 1838

It feels like a sign of the times. Coin & Curio on Pearl Street just closed, and a footwear shop will take its place. Monkey paws, serpent wings, elk teeth and bottled baby octopi. Where have all those strange objects gone? Maybe to Mr. Greenwood's, where they'll blend right in.

Uncle Octavius has made a few purchases at Coin & Curio over the years and recently donated them to our Museum. Is any Bostonian as debonair? He wore an elegant sapphire-blue waistcoat and carried his silver-handled walking stick. (I had no idea—inside is a short dagger that he uses to smite the occasional rabbit for stew.)

A group of us crowded round as he unpacked each object.

"Coiled snakes, anyone?" The label identified the twisted clump as "coiled snakes," but Uncle O knew better when he bought them. They were ammonites in rocks. "Or perhaps you'd care for some Stone Age bugs?" Again, the label lied. The "bugs" were extinct trilobites.

As for the next item, seemingly a basketful of darning needles, the label spoke the truth—fox penises! Shirly, our part-time librarian, twittered.

The last item Uncle O unwrapped was a large gray cluster tagged as "dragon spittle."

"In actuality, this is whale poop. And, I'll add, a very valuable kind of whale poop—truly a collector's item—and it enters into why several of us decided to launch the Linnaean Society of New England, the precursor to the Boston Society of Natural History. An institution that, as most of you know, failed miserably in a few short years."

We sat down around my desk, everyone wanting to hear Uncle O's full account.

"Well, one day—this was all the way back in 1814—I was poking around in Coin & Curio, and spied this—'dragon spittle,' my foot!—and recognized it as ambergris. Sometimes when a sperm whale swallows a squid, the squid's beak becomes lodged in the whale's gut and collects a gummy substance around it, then it finally gets expelled. Ages ago, an alchemist determined that this substance is a fabulous fixative for perfume. Perfumes made with it remain on the nape of a woman's neck for far longer than most scents. Which is why a big clump of ambergris is worth a pretty penny![15]

"When I saw this rarity so ridiculously labelled, it was upsetting. Those of us who collect natural riches want them placed in their rightful context, and we were tired of the *what-is-it?* confusion that our otherwise intelligent city was grappling with. Misidentified specimens were everywhere, in our museums as well as our antique stores and curiosity shops. But it went much further. The ignorance surrounding local species was also extraordinary. Even though the Indians shared their knowledge of Nature, we didn't listen closely, and the natives also weren't that exact when describing living things.

"The names of birds—they often arose from their color: *Redbird, Bluebird, Whitebird, Blackbird.*

"No one had anything like a general knowledge of the birds over our heads, of the fishes in our rivers and bays, of the shells on our beaches, of the lower tribes of animals both in air and in sea. So little was known about the wildlife outside our door, it was hard to even know how much or how little was known.[16]

"When we began our Linnaean Society, we wanted to be faithful to Carl Linnaeus and his system of classification, so we threw out a challenge to our members: Go out and find specimens from all six categories: plant, mineral, quadruped, bird, fish and reptile, insects and vermes. Young and old collected and collected—and collected—without restraint.

"It wasn't long before the new Society began to crumble under the weight of so many acquisitions. Along with stuffed this and mounted that, we even accepted live animals. The commodore of the *Constitution* contributed two Brazilian tigers; another captain donated a bear.[17] There followed a lion, a cougar, and unusual birds from France and Africa. As you might guess, these poor creatures weren't properly cared for and didn't survive for very long.

"In that I was treasurer, I tried to warn the other directors of pending financial doom, but they paid no heed. After I resigned, the situation grew ugly. The larger the collection, the more objects for visitors to examine, but the costlier the whole enterprise became. Decay set in and just about everything died on the vine."

WINTER, 1895

You have to realize, Sophie, naturalists didn't start the Linnaean Society of New England. If they had, it might have fared better.

By the 1820s, there weren't many full-time naturalists rooting around yet—although their numbers would increase as industries expanded and family wealth increased. (In earlier centuries in Europe, examiners of Nature had been looked upon as unbalanced, even deranged—and those suspicions still lingered.) More wealth would mean more leisure time for exploring Nature. But right then, most men still had to work to put food on the table. While you might call Uncle Octavius an amateur naturalist, he was a lawyer who enjoyed collecting eggs and minerals in his spare time. So it was with the Society's other found-ers—physicians, businessmen and lawyers who explored Nature on Saturdays and Sunday afternoons, and took a keen interest in medicinal plant and animal substances. They couldn't skimp on their daytime jobs to properly care for the Linnaean Society; they lacked funds to pay a manager; and, not to forget, they knew precious little about how to preserve natural specimens.

In the end, they underestimated what the new Society would require of them.

Other natural history groups, both at home and abroad, were failing for similar reasons. The amount of wildlife collected and lost in those days was staggering. Who noticed the strain on natural resources? Why would anyone care? Nature was viewed as an immense system that replenished itself. It never ran out. When people finally began realizing that certain populations were in decline, some collectors greedily shot, netted and bagged whatever individuals were left, extinguishing some species all the faster.

(September 24, 1838 letter continued)

"The Linnaean Society of New England lasted barely eight years. It was kaput by 1822." Uncle O shook his head, still rattled by that dark period. "You would have thought we had learned a lesson or two. But then, during the winter of 1829-30, something reminded us that the *what-exactly-is-it?* confu-sion was still running rampant, still needed to be confronted.

"That something was a singular display downtown: 'The Skeleton of a Behemoth.' Its bones supposedly had been found protruding from a ridge close to the mouth of the Mississippi, and the exhibitor was taking full advantage, charging a hefty admission fee. 'Come inspect a creature more enormous than an elephant, more mammoth than a Mammoth. Limited engagement!'[18]

"The exhibit hall was mobbed for days. I'm sure the crowds would have kept coming had it not been for a letter from Dr. Wyman, the distinguished physician, that appeared in the Boston Courier a week later. "The community is being deceived. The bones on view belong to a Whale, *not* a Behemoth." The exhibit abruptly closed and the con artist vanished, never to be seen in these parts again.

"Is it any surprise that once again we felt an urgent need to start a natural history society? To crack down on swindlers and protect the gullible public, all in the name of science! The Boston Natural History Society's first location was in the basement of the Boston Athenaeum on Pearl Street, only a few doors down from Coin & Curio.

"So you see, all the truths of Nature within these walls came to be here because of untruths like dragon spittle and behemoth bones. That should be reassuring to all of us."

I asked Uncle Octavius how he and his colleagues could be sure this second attempt would succeed when the first one hadn't?[19]

He shrugged. "The need to know, I guess. By then, Boston was turning into a world center for medicine, education and commerce. More than ever the city needed a place where the public could go to inspect natural objects, learn about them. Family fortunes were blossoming, and we had faith that the funds would follow."

Scientific inquiry was gaining ground, and Bostonians were hungry for revelations. Where does the Redbird spend its winter? Do fish sleep? What accounts for the steady beat of a heart?

WINTER, 1895

Back then, Sophie, if an American researcher had questions about a specimen found in the field, the advice of Europeans was often sought, since their collections were much older and their studies went back centuries. But even overseas, a closer understanding of Nature was hampered by the lack of factual reports and visual aids. Remember, aside from drawings, and the rudimentary camera obscura and the camera lucida, both of which cast images on paper that an artist could trace over, there was little precise data about specific markings that distinguished, say, a thrush from a warbler, or a frog from a toad.

No wonder swindlers selling imitations were everywhere. And yet, on both sides of the Atlantic, honest errors occurred as well. What immediately comes to mind is what a strange animal from faraway Africa was called—a *Camelopard*. It's understandable why a giraffe was formerly called this, given that its spots are so leopard-like, its neck and manner of kneeling so camel-like. Yet a giraffe is closely related to neither leopard nor camel, and this misnomer was telling of when science was still in its infancy. Even Linnaeus was perplexed about what to make of this towering creature, classifying it under the genus of Deer because of its satiny skin.

And there's the famous case of the *Paridisaea apoda*, the legless bird of paradise. Long ago, natives who killed these birds on islands near New Guinea cut their legs off when they shipped them to Europe, and, when they were uncrated, European naturalists were left to think that these birds had no legs, similar to a species described by Plutarch. They must stay in constant flight until they died and fell to earth. This misconception was finally corrected in 1824 when a Frenchman saw the bird in its natural habitat.

Heavens! The legless bird had legs!

Honest mistakes continue to occur. Not long ago, a collector visiting our Museum took one of our directors aside and advised him that an object labeled "petrified kidney" was a convoluted mass of quartz and moganite!"[20]

Another time, our insect curator was completely befuddled by a certain type of earwig. Descriptions of this insect were frustratingly inconsistent, until a discerning biologist in another state realized the mistake all the others were making. Added to a collection, an earwig's long body became brittle and frequently broke, and when someone tried to repair the damage, often-times the abdomen got glued *belly upward*, instead of *belly downward*, with no consensus to guide them.[21]

Once better tools came on the scene, never again would Nature be so thoroughly mysterious. The *what-exactly-is-it?* confusion would blow away. But right then in the 1830s, before Daguerre photographed the mandibles of a grasshopper, everywhere you traveled there was a flower waiting to be classified, a fish or bird waiting to be identified, a puzzle waiting to be solved.

September 27, 1838

On Tuesday, as I was leaving the Society, I nearly collided with a freckled-faced man who came dashing in at a great velocity for a meeting with Dr. Binney. He apologized profusely, for he really did come flying around the corner.

"Catharine, here's someone you should meet!" Dr. Binney insisted. I didn't catch the stranger's name, but, when he learned I was a Pickering, a younger cousin of the zoologist assisting Capt. Wilkes, he was quick to exclaim, "An immense pleasure!"—a mark of his esteem for you, Cousin, since he doesn't know me from Adam—and spoke of how "justice was finally served" now that a voyage to the Southern Ocean was certain to validate Capt. John Symmes's theory.

He's plainly a disciple of the late Captain Symmes and thoroughly acquainted with the Captain's reasons for believing Earth to be a hollow sphere. "I've wagered my gold pocket watch that Wilkes' fleet will locate the southern polar entrance to the inner land.

"Capt. Symmes charted its longitude, so there should be no confusion as to where the passage lies. None whatsoever!"

He made it sound like such a foregone conclusion, I pictured your fleet sailing down a narrowing fjord straight into the center of Earth. And that worried me. Because how would you get out?

WINTER, 1895

Sophie, I have no idea as to the identity of the freckled-faced stranger Catharine nearly collided with that day. However, his hero, Capt. John Cleaves Symmes, needs an introduction. This man Symmes was responsible for such a curious footnote in American history, you might think someone had made him and his strange idea up, but for a coincidental crossing of paths. John James Audubon, then a struggling artist, happened to draw Symmes in 1820, his portrait providing a trustworthy glimpse of this long-nosed man. At the time, Audubon was making a modest living sketching newsworthy faces for the Western Museum in Cincinnati, and Symmes had become newsworthy due to the circular he had sent to statesmen in America and Europe advising them of his Hollow Earth theory:

"*Be aware*: Our Earth is a hollow sphere. *Be aware*: Openings at each pole, to the north and to the south, lead to an inner world fed by fresh water and filled with lush vegetation, a world that, while absent of people at the present time, might be made inhabitable."

At first, his "Holes in The Poles Theory" bore the brunt of jokes and derision. However, bit by bit Symmes, who was Kentucky-born and had proven himself to be a brave and honorable Army captain during the Revolutionary War, and who tirelessly gave lectures and wrote articles explaining his theory, won over supporters. He didn't seem like a madman, people decided. His ability to make a convincing case for his theory, and to believe in it so thoroughly himself, was simply a sign of how little was known about our planet in those days. Hardly anyone was familiar with the animals that ran across its surface, so it followed that whatever lay hidden below ground was anyone's guess.

Encouraged, Symmes petitioned Congress for funds for an exploratory voyage. If the polar routes were found, American merchants might use them to their advantage and profit handsomely, he urged. When Congress turned him down, his followers took up the cause. In 1828, an expedition set sail and the sailors finally reached the South Pole, but any further progress was halted by thick ice. The entrance to the underworld was as blocked "as the cave in the forty thieves, and what is worse, they could contrive no plan to open it," mocked a reporter back in Washington D.C.[22]

After Symmes died in 1829, his theory faded from view. He deserves credit, nevertheless, for stirring up interest in a Voyage of Discovery to the Southern Ocean. When the long-anticipated Exploring Expedition at last set sail, the Navy's chief goals for captain and crew were to investigate routes of commerce, bolster relations with distant populations, chart major whaling grounds, and, in the words of the Secretary of the Navy, "extend the bounds of science, and promote the acquisition of knowledge."

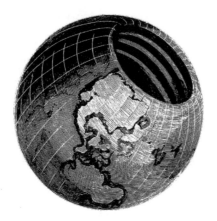

Symmes's "Hollow Earth" theory

By 1838, there weren't many people left who believed in Symmes and his theory, but clearly some devotees, such as the stranger Cath encountered, still carried the torch.

When I was a boy and we had company over, we would spin the globe in the drawing room and calculate where Cousin Charles and his band of Scientifics might be at that very moment. Once I was tucked in and said my prayers, in my dreams I'd see them opening a polar door and plunging into a steamy Inner World of bubbling hot springs beneath a green sky alive with butterflies as big as birds.

The Voyage had everyone's imagination working overtime—Cath's as much as mine.

(September 27 1838 letter continued)

Cousin, you've praised Capt. Symmes's theory, not because you believe a word of it, but because it gave the Wilkes fleet an excuse to explore the Southern Ocean. I was curious to hear more from the stranger, and asked him a lot of questions, which he seemed happy to answer.

—Yes, in 1818, to drum up support for his endeavor, Capt. Symmes sent a circular to statesmen and nobility. He and one-hundred men would leave Siberia in the fall season, he proposed, and with reindeer and sleighs they would make their way across the frozen sea to where, just north of latitude 82, the Captain was certain they would encounter the North

Pole's opening marked by a large river rushing inward. "We shall find a warm and rich land, stocked with thrifty vegetables and animals, if not people"—those were his very words.[23]

—Several pieces of evidence attest to the Inner World and its polar holes that cannot be accounted for any other way. Consider the northern entrance. The driftwood that every year ends up on the shores of Iceland, Greenland and Siberia, which resembles no other timber ever seen, it must come from the far north. It must therefore originate from Earth's torrid interior and escape through the polar hole into arctic seas. And those northern currents—their counter-clockwise and clockwise flows can only be explained by a cavity at the northern pole. Within the arctic circles there is ice-free ocean and a strange warmth, which must indicate an opening into Earth's warm interior. And not to be overlooked are the large herds of reindeer that leave Hudson Bay as winter approaches and move north, only to return in spring with plentiful young who are plump and healthy. What do they feed on so far north? Certainly not frozen moss. No, it must be vegetation cultivated year-round by the luxuriant climate of the Inner World that sustains them.

That evening I asked Father about Symmes and his theory.

"Nat Bowditch always referred to it as the 'Yawning Hole Theory.'"

And with that, Father gave a big yawn, kissed me on the head and shuffled off to bed.

September 30, 1838

I have another Troc'ulus saved for you. It is straight from a young physician from Scotland who recently visited the collection.

Some years ago in Selkirkshire, this man's uncle, a farmer, went out to meet with one of his shepherds. An inch or two of new snow covered the ground, and as the farmer climbed a small hill, he crossed the track of a black-tailed weasel. Curious to see where it led, he followed it to where it ended abruptly and where, he could tell by different markings, a pair of grouse had been sitting. At first he was bewildered. What had happened to the weasel? There was no hole nearby to jump down, or any close bough it could have leapt on. It was as though it had vanished into thin air, which, the farmer finally realized, must have happened. The weasel must have leapt onto one of the birds, who rose frantically in the air caught in the stoat's clutches, until it came struggling down in field or forest as its life ebbed away. The farmer met someone who had actually seen a weasel performing this stunt. It had no problem landing safely, and with a good meal in tow.

You and I have often discussed how brutal one animal can be to another. But even this conniving weasel doesn't compare to our own kind. Yesterday's paper carried an account by a hunter recently back from India. He and his companions met up with a Bengal tiger one moonlit night and were struck dumb by the tiger's incredible beauty, and yet they fired. To praise such a superb animal and then kill it—doesn't he hear his own hypocrisy? I like hunters less and less, I find.

On to more pleasant thoughts. Everyone is in fine spirits, particularly Mary. She's soon off to Italy, and we're all terribly jealous. I'm feeling rundown but have only myself to blame. I've taken on a third pupil, Sarah Apley, and Dr. Binney has asked for more hours, and I'm happy to oblige. There have been some late nights as well. Your mother and the Nichols rode down from Salem for the opening of a new comedy at the Tremont, and when we returned to Beacon Street, Father poured nightcaps and we stayed up discussing why the play wasn't funny at all, until the wick went down!

Capt. Waterman informs us that the *Nightingale* is preparing to leave for South America, so I will run our packet down to the docks, and hope it finds its way to you. It's too soon to expect news of the Squadron. But we search the papers every day, afraid to miss the smallest mention.

Know you are constantly in the thoughts of those who pray. And those who don't.

Cath

To Charles Pickering aboard the USS Vincennes
From Catharine Pickering, Boston

October 15, 1838

Dearest Pickle, so missed,

We mark each nautical mile of your voyage on a large map in the parlor. If the fleet's progress has proven steady, you'll soon cross the Equator—perhaps it's already off your stern— and then must cross another substantial stretch of sea before making landfall in Brazil.

Here at home, there have been almost too many events and obligations. I'm ready for winter, and soft snow as high as the back gate to mute the noise of carriages and wrap the city in peace. Maybe then I'd regain my stamina. I'm still short on energy, and consume large amounts of cod liver oil. Does anything taste worse?

Last week Dr. Binney shared his ticket to a show of Mr. Audubon's impressive *Birds of America* portfolio at the Athenaeum.[24] Our Natural History Society also subscribes to the artist's engravings but displays them on the front table. At the Athenaeum, the entire flock hangs from the walls, as if airborne, each bird life-sized[25] What artistic gumption. A whooping crane is bent low as it seizes a lizard, a ploy to get the whole bird on the page. It works!

A rumor circulated that the painter would attend. I looked around the room for someone finely tailored, with a sharp chin, dark searching eyes and long dark ringlets—until I ran into Dr. Parkman who dispelled the rumor. Dr. Parkman is serving as the painter's Boston agent now he's retired. Who better for the job. He has a wide circle of friends and thinks Audubon the best painter in the world.

We paused together in front of the muscular flight of Audubon's golden eagle. "Look how real Mr. Audubon's birds are! Mr. Wilson's birds, they have the stiff profiles of marching Egyptians in comparison." He kept his voice low, knowing the room was filled with Wilson enthusiasts who had come to judge whether Mr. Audubon was as good as advertised and any contest for Mr. Wilson, the older favorite. I agreed entirely. You could nearly feel the breath of the bird we stood next to.

"All these birds"—the Doctor made an embracing gesture—"they so narrowly missed being here." I asked him what he meant, and he recounted how the artist had nearly met his maker not once but three times.

Audubon nearly died when his mother, a chambermaid who had had a dalliance with his father, a French sea captain, died giving birth to him. Then, arriving in America to oversee his father's property in Pennsylvania, he was stricken with yellow fever. Fortunately, he was nursed back to health by two Quaker women who ran a boardinghouse. Then, a few winters later, he and several friends were skating homeward on Perkiomen Creek after a day of hunting, when John James, who was leading the way through the gathering dusk, abruptly fell through an air-hole, the icy water closing over his head and the swift current dragging him downstream, until, just as abruptly, he popped up through another air-hole, half-frozen but alive. By all rights, this might have been his death.

We all remember five years ago when Mr. Audubon and his family were wintering in Boston, and he collapsed with a fever after finishing the very bird the doctor and I were mesmerized by, the golden eagle. For his care, Dr. Parkman received a rare gift from the artist, a set of Mr. Audubon's *Ornithological Biography*—with a feather glued inside.

The artist also named a newly discovered marsh bird after the doctor— "Parkman's wren."

"I feel immortal!" beamed Dr. Parkman.

After so many near misses, Mr. Audubon must as well.

WINTER, 1895

Sophie bear, as it turns out, Dr. Parkman wasn't nearly immortal enough. Eleven years after Audubon named a wren after him, there was the matter of his disappearance from the streets of Boston, and the discovery of his bones in the laboratory oven of a colleague at Harvard Medical School.[26] Most everyone is familiar with the grizzly details. Dr. Parkman's regrettable mistake was to loan money to John Webster, a professor of chemistry. Your father did a fine job of employing dental work to identify the remains. The cruelest irony, I've always thought, was that the doctor was murdered on land he had donated to Harvard for medical care.

I'm not sure you're aware of this, but our Charles and John James Audubon, despite an age difference of twenty years, were well acquainted. Most naturalists were back then, the field was so small and intimate. Audubon spoke of Charles as "his learned friend" and often went to him for his bird expertise. Once, he didn't realize the bird he had shot represented a new species of thrush, "until my friend Dr. Pickering enlightened me," he later wrote.

During his years-long project of drawing every bird nesting in North America, Audubon visited Boston on at least three occasions, sometimes for long durations.

"Ah! I think often of the friends who afforded me so much pleasure in this beautiful city…. her Adamses, her Perkins, her Everetts, Peabodys, Quinceys, Storeys, Paines and Pickerings, whose public and private life presents all that we deem estimable."

My parents saw a fair amount of John James and his wife Lucy when they were in town, and once, returning home from a reception for the artist, Father announced, "That man's breath smells worse than the Bay at low tide!" This was so like your great-great grandfather, always eager to pull a luminary off his pedestal. Mother said the artist was attractively dressed in a dark frock coat, blue hunting shirt and velvet vest, and a small smile on her lips told me that she'd been taken by the artist's charm and dark good looks, which may have explained why Father was especially grumpy that evening.

In the mid-1830s, after Congress finally voted to subsidize a voyage to the South Seas, the Secretary of the Navy's first thought was that Audubon, Charles Pickering and Thomas Nuttall would make a perfect team of naturalists for the mission. But Audubon, who was over the age of fifty by then, felt he was too old for the voyage. "I wish to God I were young once more! How delighted I would be to go in such company of learned men, dear friends."

He hoped the Expedition would succeed beyond all expectations. "For the sake of science! for the honor of our beloved country!"[27]

I met the artist just once, at Dr. Parkman's funeral in 1849, by which time Audubon's attractive robustness was gone. He was rail-thin, disheveled and nearly blind. I was with my parents, and as the artist passed us, a woman seized his shoulder and attempted to make small talk. How vividly she recollected the summer day he had come to her family's estate in Essex and shot two fine peregrine falcons. Audubon stopped mid-stride and turned his vacant eyes toward her. By then, along with his fading physical condition, he was straying into senility. Yet he apparently recalled the occasion, for the memory made him quite cross.

"I was foolish back then," he exclaimed, "and isn't it ironic, I've reached an age when my hair and teeth are falling out, and I only see shadows. Yet my heart has grown, and I value the worth of a bird as I never properly did years ago. So please do me the favor of forgetting that day and my regrettable behavior."

And out the door he went, gripping the shoulder of a son who led the way.

Two years later, at age sixty-five, he died. He was buried near his homestead on the banks of the Hudson in upper Manhattan. I visited his grave years later and was glad to find the birdsong, profuse and cheerful, rising above the harsh noise of automobiles.

October 20, 1838

Our museum and library on Tremont Street are bursting at the seams—15,459 objects and counting. We are so bursting that the directors have begun plans for another move.

At least our cabinet is more organized than the jumble one finds at Salem's East India Marine Society. I spent a few nights on Broad Street last week, returning for books & linens and to clean the gardens, and made a point of visiting their museum. It's as though someone turned the building upside down and gave it a vigorous shake! Iron spears from China sit next to wooden stilts from the south Pacific. A parasol from Calcutta rests next to a Venetian glass chandelier. Native lip ornaments sit beside—and I'm entirely serious—a hideous-looking waistcoat made from the intestines of a Sea-Lion!

One ship left off a chunk of pavement from ancient Troy, or so the crew claimed.

I managed to locate your childhood collection of insects, which, I'm sorry to say, looks moth-eaten, quite literally. After considerable hunting, I also located the rattlesnake skin and Algerine rifle that Grandfather donated. Father says that with commerce shifting to deep-water harbors to the south, Boston and New York will receive more and more objects, Salem fewer and fewer. Maybe this will give the Marine Society a chance to catch its breath & organize its sprawling muddle.

Dr. Binney led a useful staff meeting on Monday. He implored our curators to be vigilant about separating the wheat from the chaff, the educational from the purely entertaining, the authentic from the outlandish. The public has a ravenous appetite for strange objects, he warned. Whatever you do, he said, don't forget that our mission is to educate with real phenomena, not to amuse with oddities or accidents of Nature.

Amusement! That's where Cincinnati's Western Museum is headed; the American Philosophical Society's cabinet as well. Their goal is to entertain— even horrify—their patrons. And Mr. Greenwood's New England Museum, it's the same as when we were children clinging to our mothers. Remember that cheerless dwarf by the name of Stevens? Remember that hideous "Vampyre of the Ocean" in the lower hall?[28]

Mr. Greenwood's finances never recovered from the fire years back, and I hear his museum's contents will soon be conveyed to Moses Kimball, proprietor of the Lowell Museum. He plans to open a new establishment, the Boston Museum. Everyone wonders what direction it will take. Probably more of the same, since oddities and amusement sell tickets.

"No Siamese calves, please!" Dr. Binney advised the curators. "No three-eyed badgers! Normal specimens should be enough to sell tickets." He acknowledged that our cabinet holds the token oddity— the two-headed snake, for instance. The dirty-brown fellow is soon headed to the Society for Medical Improvement for analysis. This seems the best use for him—what can he tell us about ordinary snakes?[29]

Speaking of Greenwood's, a worker there dropped a mouse into the terrarium that houses the museum's three rattlesnakes. He wanted to test their temperament.[30] No sooner did the mouse land in this precarious position, than the resident cat leapt into the box, caught the mouse and leapt out. The snakes didn't react to either intruder, and those watching this funny sight wondered if they were asleep.

WINTER, 1895

The mere thought of Mr. Greenwood's New England Museum still gives me the willies. It lay around the corner from the Boston Society of Natural History, and what a weird and wonderful place it was. When it opened in 1818, it held both natural curiosities and a fair amount of fine art, for Nathan Greenwood was both a portraitist and an art collector. Cases of birds, preserved reptiles and insects, a stuffed elephant and a stuffed moose, unusual clocks and mirrors along with relics from the failed Linnaean Society shared its rooms with oils of renowned individuals. The handsome full-length portraits of Emperor Alexander of Russia and his empress come to mind. As time went on, more and more *objets extraordinaires* were added as well as a Marine Room with sea monsters and exotic fish. Here again, too many objects and too few funds may have put Mr. Greenwood's collection on shaky ground.

Then came the fire in 1832 caused by a crack in the chimney. My family had just visited Mr. Greenwood's the week before, and the place filled me with such dread that when the fire occurred, I hoped everything inside had burned up—the upright bear at the entrance; all the fusty-smelling creatures in the monkey room; and, strangest of all, the tortured-looking "Mermaid" that gave me bad dreams for a solid week.[31]

This was the same famous "Feejee" mermaid that later turned up in just about every museum in the country that showcased oddities. She—more correctly *it*—was brought back from the western Pacific by a Boston sea captain, Samuel Eades, and for many a year it represented the city's most hideous, and therefore, its most popular attraction. In 1821, Capt. Eades, who was commander and one-eighth owner of the *Pickering*, a schooner named after an English branch of Pickerings unknown to us, had saved the crew of a sinking Dutch man-of-war in the vicinity of the Dutch East Indies, and officials in Batavia were so grateful, they spoke of giving Capt. Eades a sizeable reward.

It was while Capt. Eades was still in those waters, anticipating this gift, that a group of merchants took him to see a dried, shrunken figure that had landed in the nets of a fisherman off the coast of China.[32] This rarity, this possible link between fish and terrestrials, can be yours for 5000 Spanish dollars, they offered.

Their high asking price should have scared off Capt. Eades, if the mermaid's questionable authenticity—or her unsettling looks—hadn't. She was about three feet long with a baboon-like head covered by inky black hair. Her upper torso, possessing human-like arms and breasts, was attached to a scaly body that fluted into a large curving tail similar to mermaids in picture books. This mermaid's proportions were skewed, however, and she wore a terrified look, as if she had died in great agony.

The award money never actually materialized. But that didn't stop Capt. Eades from selling the *Pickering* and purchasing the mermaid with the proceeds. Normally a cautious sort, he must have tasted the money to be raked in from exhibiting such a bizarre relic. No record exists of how his partner in London, the ship's principal owner, took the news, or if Eades was able to completely settle that debt. After that, his *Maid of the Sea* exhibit drew large audiences both at home and abroad, yet faced mounting competition. Similar amalgams of monkey heads sewn to fish bodies were turning up in major cities everywhere, and at some point, after Eades died, maybe close to penniless, others continued to exhibit his gruesome treasure, among them, Mr. Greenwood and the most notorious charlatan of all, P.T. Barnum.

Fabrications like the Feejee Mermaid were inevitable. So little was known about the natural phenomena of air, land and sea, the door lay open for just about any contrivance. Once the world was better explored, and its life forms officially recorded, only then would people know what was real and what wasn't. Only then would the curiosity over curiosities begin to subside.

October 26, 1838

Yesterday was tutoring day. The girls were angels, but cousin Oliver was up to his tricks. I arrived at the Meeting House to find he'd strung a cord between the boot-scraper and a lamppost, nearly tripping Edith Codman as she passed. As you know, she's a woman of wide girth, and although she stayed upright, she was hardly amused. Oliver's mother needs to apply more discipline; and his father is away so much, he spoils the boy when he's home.

Daniel Webster visited the Society yesterday and asked after you. He donated a pair of oystercatchers.[33] They are handsome, although their feathers are marred with shot. And since they are dead, they make me sad. It's hard to hope for a better world when intelligent humans like Mr. Webster steal from Nature whatever and whenever they please.

Your friend Rev. William Peabody is a frequent user of the Society's library, and I've enjoyed getting to know him. He's close to finishing his report on the birds of Massachusetts for the state legislature. You know his calm exterior. But when the subject turns to the bird world, he grows as animated as a sparrow in a spring rain. One interesting outcome of his report was his investigation, on behalf of the state's farmers, into birds that are detrimental to crops. His findings aren't what many farmers want to hear, since his report concluded that no birds rob our fields and gardens so badly that they should be exterminated.

"Some are occasionally troublesome," he admitted to me. "But, do what we may, we cannot prevent their depredations. If we shoot them, we only gratify our revengeful feeling, since new reinforcements stand ready to replace those that fall."[34]

He maintains that the Lord has put birds on Earth to keep insects in check as well as to scatter seed and fill the landscape with beauty and energy. That farmers persist in pointing their guns at the sky sickens him. Which is why he joined a local walking club called "Hunting Without A Gun." It was started by a young man by the name of James Cutting, a member of the Society, and Rev. Peabody means to introduce us some day.

Who is this Mr. Cutting? I asked.

"Well, in my opinion, he's just about the smartest whippersnapper in Boston. He's very technically able, very intuitive. A bit different, really"—the Reverend gave me a wink—"something of a freethinker like you." I took this as a compliment. I don't know Reverend Peabody very well, but evidently something about me sticks out a little crookedly. I'm curious to meet this Mr. Cutting.

May an albatross flying overhead be your guide,

Your fond cousin

To Charles Pickering aboard the USS Vincennes
From Catharine Pickering, Boston

November 5, 1838

Dear Pick,

Reverend Peabody was at the Museum again, this time with his friend in tow, the young man he has spoken about in glowing terms, James Ambrose Cutting. Are you acquainted with him?

Mr. Cutting is a young inventor—he must be several years my junior—who already has made a name for himself. He moved to Boston from New Hampshire, where he formerly worked in his father's plating business. Once here, he took a job as a pension agent, and while he didn't care for the work, he managed to rapidly acquire a fortune and now devotes himself to his real passion, inventing.[35]

Yesterday he gave the Society a solar microscope of his own design. He has another at home that he uses for examining tiny freshwater animalcules. He dissects them—with a cat's whisker!—and watches them regrow their missing half in just a few days. I asked this young carrot top—he has hair as orange as the setting sun—what makes them so resilient? He motioned with his hands and replied, speaking so fast that I couldn't follow. Something about their tissue.

Does he speak rapidly because he's shy and wants to be done with it? No, I think it's because he's intense and wired that way.

Mother says I'm too critical of men. I suspect she's right. Most seem completely taken up by their business, their livestock, their carriage—the opposite of you and Father, who are inquisitive and perceptive about everything around you. So, too, this Mr. Cutting, whose eyes moved quickly, taking in every detail. We were in the second-floor hall. The winter sun was streaming through the tall windows, and, as the clocks struck noon, he noticed the sun throwing a large shadow of the rhinoceros sculpture onto the far wall. It happens exactly at noon in the fall and winter seasons; an animal shadow so large and diffuse, visitors usually miss it. But Mr. Cutting noticed it immediately, and chatted about a rhinoceros infant he had seen at London's zoo, again talking so fast, his words were a blur.

His gaze alighted on my boots. You know my habit of wearing knee-highs rather than stylish ankle boots that freeze the toes. "Practical to a fault," Mother chides. His glance was approving, I hope.

Before Mr. Cutting left, young Henry Thoreau arrived, and slowly unfolded his handkerchief to reveal a clump of tiny seeds. He discovered an orchid this summer in Concord that he's certain is uncommon, and wants the Society to preserve its seeds in our vault. He sprinkled a few onto our palms—Mr. Cutting's palm is very broad and muscular, I noticed. My seeds are now stored in a small tin. You'll have to help me grow them.

One last piece of news—a little gossip to enliven your life at sea! Ernest Hooper and Sarah Wigglesworth have run off together. Yes, *that* Ernest, the upright churchgoer. And *that* Sarah, innocent as a lamb. Well, maybe not. First Edward reported his wife missing, and then Victoria reported her husband missing, which began the rumor that maybe they had gone missing together! Peter Wick reported that he saw them climbing aboard an early coach for New York, and Alma Anderson, Sarah's closest confidante, shared that last night the couple boarded *Starlight* for Trieste.

Good for them! I can't help but think. Each was probably miserable—Ernest putting up with a wife who insists on Parisian fineries; Sarah, a saint to a husband who dallies with the chambermaid. Though they've left family and friends behind, they'll start over and make new connections. There's an attitude that people stay married to the same person and routine, but why, why if they are miserable and see the faintest chance for a happier future?

November 10, 1838

Time and again, Father has been asked to dust off the lecture he delivered on telegraphic systems five years ago. Perhaps it was you who finally persuaded him to, for he gave the lecture last Friday before a rapt audience at the Boston Athenaeum.[36] Every seat was taken. Mr. Morse's public demonstration of his electromagnetic telegraph last January has validated Father's years-old prediction of an invention of this type, and reporters are finally catching up and quoting Father left and right, all of them dizzy over the "new science" of communications.

Father got across—magnificently, I thought—that telegraphic systems are as old as the desire to "talk" long-distance. Lit torches, smoke puffs, cannon blasts, signals conveyed by the arms of windmills, the flags of marine telegraphy. But these tactics, he said, will soon seem clumsy once Mr. Morse's method of sending electrical pulses over a single wire is perfected.[37]

"Isn't it to be expected," Father asked, "that the demands of business may soon lead to the establishment of telegraphic communications between our principal cities?"

Someone in the room gave a low whistle as commentary.

Father kept on: "Let's look ahead; let's prepare for when this invention will stretch between this city and New York, Philadelphia and Washington."

Once more, the low whistle sliced the air.

"The telegraph will eventually span one side of the Continent to the other. And the day will come when we'll receive intelligence from China in as short a time as it reaches us from Europe.[38]

The whistle this time lasted so long that Father gave a sharp glance around the room. I looked in the direction of the sound and noticed James Cutting seated behind old Mrs. Longfellow, and, all in a second, he caught my eye, and with a slight nod of his head, he signaled that the whistle was coming from Mrs. Longfellow. She was asleep and wheezing, I realized, and Mr. Cutting and I traded looks that came perilously close to laughter.

"We need to look ahead and prepare for the future," Father concluded.

November 15, 1838

Cousin, the week has produced more food for thought than I can swallow.

On Saturday, the day after Father's talk, Mr. Buckley, the antiquarian, spoke at the Society about previous civilizations and their responses to Nature. It was a surprise to learn that some Ancients weren't particularly curious about natural treasures. And more greedy than appreciative. One Roman emperor ordered his captains to obtain the perfect roe. Another sent his soldiers to capture birds for his aviary, beasts for his arena, fish for his fishpond. Apparently, they were too focused on war, too selfish and too preoccupied with sensual pleasures, to peer very deeply into the natural world.[39]

Then Mr. Buckley began hammering away on one certain point:

"I dare say, the world was considerably better off when Nature was underappreciated. The greater our appreciation of Nature, the more we bankrupt her reserves.

"Mr. Hodgkin's market around the corner, stocked with redbreast, pigeon and snipe *for our food*. Mr. Gray's Conservatory, overflowing with exotic plants and animals *for our amusement*. Forests to the north and west are open territory for bear and moose, hawk and bobolink *for our food and sport*.

"Even your fine cabinets here at the Society, let's face it, are replete with species robbed from the wild *for our knowledge, our enlightenment, our intellectual entertainment*.

"Us, us, us. It's not about *them* so much, is it? As we continue to pursue Nature with gun and microscope, harpoon and net, where will this genocide lead? We humans are despicable blockheads!"

From the back of the room came "Hear! Hear!" I recognized James Cutting's energetic voice. Others in the room were likely offended by Mr. Buckley's comments about our collection, yet everything he said was completely true. It is all about us, and not nearly enough about *them*.

November 16, 1838

To continue where I left off, there's no denying that Bostonians are ravenous for natural riches. We presently are in the grip of elephant-mania. Two of these beasts, brought by rail from New York, are on exhibit at the menagerie at the base of The Common. They are advertised as the first African quadrupeds in

New England, and, as you can guess, the visitor line extends down Tremont Street. (According to Father, people have short memories. He remembers Capt. Crowninshield of Salem sailing an elephant over from Bengal in 1797. "Old Bet" was showed up and down the coast.)

For time off from tutoring, I took my three charges over to see the elephants. Animals in captivity generally depress me, yet these hulks looked content enough, supplied as they were with fresh grasses and the sun streaming down through an open roof. Most impressive were their colossal feet, and the careful way they shifted their weight.

Cousin Ollie pulled his nose as he studied their trunks.

Way back in time, elephants possibly had long upper and lower jaws, I said, recalling something I'd read, and eventually the lower jaw shrank, and the upper jaw turned into a swinging trunk.

"No, that's not right!" Ollie jumped around like a blond jumping bean, and shouted out his explanation. He's at that excitable small boy phase, when they don't talk but shriek! "A baby elephant was drinking from a pond one day, and a big crocodile with big teeth caught it by its nose and tried to eat it, but the elephant didn't give up and got free. But its nose got stretched."

Bravo, Ollie! Far better than my boringly-adult explanation.

You won't be surprised to learn that every newspaper in town is full of elephant stories. Here's a clipping from yesterday's *Transcript*, to give you a chuckle.

THE
Elephant,

"Last spring, wanting to promote good relations, the mayor of a small town on the western coast of England, sent the Lord Mayor of London the first prized salmon of the season taken from the river Severn. His lordship immediately sat down and wrote a reply: 'Great appreciation for the magnificent creature that arrived yesterday. It will be hard to find, but I will soon send you an *equivalent*.' 'My goodness,' exclaimed Mayor Vigors to his wife. 'The Lord Mayor is so pleased with the salmon I sent, he is going to send me an *elephant*! What a rarity, what a gift!' The Lord Mayor's handwriting contained so many perpendicular flourishes that Vigors had mistaken the most important word in the note, *equivalent*, which was meant to convey a delicious orange fish, for a large gray quadruped. The poor man drained the town's coffers in order to build a huge shed for the animal, only to receive a superb salmon from London and discover his mistake."[40]

By now you must have finally dropped anchor off Brazil. I'm envisioning you in an azure harbor, refreshed by spring water, tropical fruits and rums. The natives you are meeting—what do they look like; what do they wear? Are they peaceful or suspicious? Welcoming, I hope, not warlike!

Cousin Ollie asked me if South Sea natives have "horse bodies." The boy is as imaginative as he is mischievous.

November 30, 1838

One gray afternoon this week, Reverend Peabody and I lingered over tea in the Society's library. The Reverend had been talking about guns, and his loathing of them, when, for no apparent reason—and yet one would emerge—he began describing an older colleague, Rev. Alexander John Forsyth of Scotland, who presides over a parish in Belhelvie near Aberdeen.

"Not many know of him, but they do his invention."

The two men met at a ministers' conclave in Aberdeen, and at other conferences, and over countless cups of tea and pints of brew, they traded their life stories. Forsyth's father, the parish's former minister, had been deeply cherished. When he dropped dead after a Presbytery meeting in 1790, his parishioners instantly transferred their devotion to his son. Fifty years have passed, and this second Forsyth, now in his eighties, still serves the same parish.[41]

"Unsparingly conscientious and helpful to those in need." That's how Rev. Peabody described his friend. The door of his cottage was always open, and yet Rev. Forsyth was no pushover. This is how he dealt with a cynical minister from York whom he didn't care for. The York minister was ready to punish a townsman for shooting deer on public lands—an act prohibited under English game laws—because, the York minister said, there was the Devil to pay. Forsyth's instant reply was, And how do you know there's a Devil? The York minister scowled, as the Devil might scowl, and never visited again, which made Rev. Forsyth count his blessings.

I was amazed to hear that the English prohibited deer hunting on public lands.[42]

"Nor are the English allowed to kill fowl on their own property," said Rev. Peabody, "unless it's a very large estate and they have a license. We Americans have this go-where-you-please-shoot-what-you-will swagger. The English, on the other hand, are beholden to game laws that reach back to feudal days when so much as killing a hare was punishable by death.

Rev. Peabody had more on his mind about his Scottish friend.

"When preparing a sermon, Rev. Forsyth was in the habit of walking up and down the lane beside his manse. In his younger days, he had a pet goose, and the goose followed close on his heels, almost stride for stride. It was all his housekeeper could do to keep the bird from trailing the Reverend to church. The goose loved the minister beyond all else, and the minister loved the goose as an equal. And yet—and this still astonishes me—one of his favorite pastimes was to hunt ducks, geese, and all kinds of other birds as well."

Rev. Peabody heaved a great sigh. I thought he had no more to say about his friend, who, like so many of us, was a living contradiction—a man of amiable character who loved a goose, but who also hunted, killed and ate geese. There was more to his story, however, and as a hard rain beat on the Society's windows, he continued, sounding increasingly glum.

"Again and again, Rev. Forsyth returned from hunting feeling peeved. As good a shot as he was, many birds escaped his aim. He blamed his gun, for as soon as he pulled the flint-lock's trigger, a puff of smoke alerted the bird, and it flew away before the lead shot reached it. Clearly the gun could be improved upon, he decided.

"He spent many hours of the day in 'the minister's Smiddy,' as his neighbors referred to his garden hut, where, donning his blacksmith's apron, he repaired locks, crafted penknives, and made and sharpened tools. He also practiced chemistry, and minerology, and was constantly mixing and grinding.

One winter he went so far as to make a charcoal prepared with soda that burned for fifteen hours, saving the poorest in his parish pennies a day. He experimented, too, with electrical current, believing that it could outperform steam as a source of power.

"Month after month he worked on a more bird-worthy fowling-piece. Why not a percussion-lock mechanism to replace the flint-lock apparatus? Why not a hammer's strike to ignite the powder instead of sparks? No flash would be emitted. The firearm would detonate faster, with more certainty of lead finding feather. He admired how his older friend, the Scotsman James Watt, had plodded through countless trials-and-errors before arriving at an improved steam engine. He admired how Edward Jenner in England had pushed forward with his vaccine for smallpox, despite the derision of nonbelievers. Corresponding with Jenner, Forsyth became thoroughly acquainted with the treatment, and when smallpox broke out in Belhelvie, he was able to jump into action and inoculate the sick girl. After her recovery, the entire parish lined up at his door to be inoculated.

"He kept his head down and plugged away at his invention, just like his friends Watt and Jenner had done. However, government officials caught wind of Forsyth's important new firearm and closeted him away in the Tower of London, away from any distractions. When the invention was finally finished, they made claims on his work and, to this day, he has never been properly reimbursed."

Rev. Peabody stood up and started pacing.

"Sportsmen were quick to adopt the percussion-lock. Not only was it faster and more accurate than the flint-lock, it was more reliable in damp weather and misfired less. Just last year—decades later—the British Army equipped its soldiers with it. I think the generals were waiting for Forsyth to die, to be sure of stealing his idea without a penny of payment!"

The Reverend sat back down and loosened his collar, a gesture that as much as said *I'm tired out by the stupid things that humans do.*

"We originally invented weapons for food and protection. Now we're better growers, and fewer threats surround us. Yet our guns keep getting more accurate and cunning. And we're stuck with this loathsome habit. Young boys sleep with a gun at their side, as if it were a dog; and they can pick off a squirrel with one shot to the head. Where will this lead? We should worry that as good reasons for guns further diminish, our insecurities will cause us to point them more at each other. We are not a nice species, let's face it."

By then it was raining so hard, the buildings across the street were gray smudges.

Did Reverend Forsyth regret the technology he had given the world?

"He doesn't regret improving the aim of soldiers. But as time has passed, he deeply regrets having improved the aim of hunters. And causing innocent wildlife to suffer. He shudders to think what an evil menace we've become."

After Rev. Peabody left, I could only sit and watch the rain falling. I don't think I've ever heard such a depressing story. A decent, kind man concocted a better firearm for killing birds, and now it has arrived on the battlefield where it makes it relatively easy to kill members of our own species? Life really isn't sacred anymore.

With love, your cousin

WINTER, 1895

Little Bear, I wish you'd known your cousin John Pickering, the lawyer-linguist. He was always one step ahead and predicted telegraphic messaging even before Samuel Morse contemplated becoming an inventor. What a boon for business-to-business relationships! For governments! For rallying troops against an enemy! He forecasted the whole business: the telegraphic equipment linking cities, the underwater Atlantic cable connecting America and Europe, the handheld devices for calling someone a city block away.

But most people had a hard time understanding what Uncle John was talking about. To most people, it sounded like Greek—a language Uncle John spoke fluently, by the way.

As for Reverend Forsyth's new firing mechanism, some people actually disapproved of faster-acting firearms. Slower mechanisms made for greater sport. The Indians had called buffleheads 'Spirit' ducks, because of how quickly they flew off at just the twang of a bow.[43] When flint-locks were surpassed, warning sounds for wildlife vanished.

To Charles Pickering aboard the USS Vincennes
From Catharine Pickering, Boston

December 10, 1838

Favorite Cousin,

Father's friend Randall Adams of Salem joined us for supper last night. He's certain that tantalizing sightings of a Southern Continent below the known territories will be confirmed by your Squadron, as long as thick ice doesn't prevent a close sighting. I had no idea so many claims have been made in the past. He regaled us with stories of captains thinking they saw a coastline far below Cape Horn from afar, only to admit, because the ice kept them at a distance, they couldn't be certain.

"Down there, the sea and sky blend into a ghostly white wall," he described. "You could be in heaven."

We think Mr. Adams expected your mother to be present. He wore a floral-patterned silk brocade waistcoat and smelled strongly of scented lotion. If you worry about Lurena being too much on her own, between Mr. Adams' devoted attention, your brother's weekend visits, and the wandering eye of half of Salem's male population, she is better looked after than if she had a husband. Mr. Adams related—nearly with a husband's pride—that Lurena's raspberry bushes produced berries through Thanksgiving, and that her squash won a blue ribbon this summer at the Fair. He was one of the judges, naturally.

I never have to look far for a Troc'ulus for you. Someone is always wandering into the Society with one on the tip of his tongue. This was told by Mr. Higgins of Marblehead, a strange upsetting battle that he and his wife saw unfold from their drawing room, which faces the harbor.

Their attention was taken by a large, particularly active cormorant—the way he raised himself perpendicular to the water's surface, shot down forcibly, and reappeared with a small fish that he swallowed head-first. It wasn't long before he dove down again—cormorants are restless, says Mr. Higgins, and hardly ever come to a stop the way ducks, teal, and wigeons do—and this time he reappeared with a large eel part in and part out of his gullet. For the next half hour, Mr. Higgins swears, a contest raged between the cormorant and the serpent. The cormorant, its body arching and contorting, would nearly succeed in swallowing the eel, only for the eel to reemerge from the bird's mouth, wiggling furiously toward an escape. The bird, shaking and shuddering, once more would nearly claim success. Once more the eel would wiggle back up, its tail at one point hanging a foot out of its bedeviler's mouth, until finally, its strength spent, it disappeared for good.[44]

Are you shuddering?! Can you imagine a worse death than dissolving inside another animal's stomach?

December 14, 1838

You'll like to hear that your brother has a new bounce to his step, and we believe it's due to spirited, fun-loving Charlotte Hammond. For the first time since Edward lost Sally, his smile is bright, his pocket handkerchief folded just so.

Another servant of a gentleman visiting Boston from the South has disappeared, this time right from under the noses of the bellhops at the Tremont House. The chief engineer of the Portsmouth and Roanoke Rail Road was in town for business, accompanied by his wife and their maid, whom the family has great affection for. She helped raise their five children. While the papers refer to it as a "kidnapping," this woman will probably quickly adapt to, and savor, her new freedom. Newspapers constantly warn Southern gentlemen against bringing their servants north of the Potomac. Let's hope Southern gentlemen continue to overlook this advice. And that numerous other servants get whisked away to a life they can call their own.

Boston is experiencing colder than usual temperatures, but I'm certain the woman who vanished is warmly cared for and well fed.

Your loving Cath

To Charles Pickering aboard the USS Vincennes
From Catharine Pickering, Boston

January 20, 1839

Dearest Pick,

Good news, finally! The returning *Minerva* reports that the Wilkes fleet, when last observed, was serenely at anchor in Rio de Janeiro's harbor.[45] How long we've waited for a sighting! *Minerva's* sailors, however, are a gossipy lot, and we wonder if we can trust the stories they spread around town. They say that most every Scientific has clashed with Capt. Wilkes, and that he and Capt. Couthouy in particular don't see eye-to-eye.

And can it be true that Capt. Wilkes forgot to purchase microscopes when he went to Europe to buy instruments for the voyage, and that you and the other Scientifics are without them? They say that your captain has little interest in natural studies; that he keeps you and the other naturalists from going ashore with the rest of the crew, afraid of what strange specimens you'll bring back. Really?! If all of this is true, you, more than anyone, have the power to persuade Capt. Wilkes of the importance of observing species in the intimacy of their surroundings. Your respect for Nature has always been infectious!

Here at home, my wish has been granted. Boston has been walloped by a great snowstorm, its drifts higher than the garden gate. With schools cancelled, throngs of delirious children, accompanied by mothers and nannies, have been coasting down the Common's long diagonal, screams erupting and snowballs flying. Oliver, his mother tells me, packed his snowballs with ice and gave a small friend a bloody lip. Our cousin, I'm afraid, is himself icy and cold, a combative little terror who hasn't received enough affection from parents who constantly spar. If only he would thaw. That's become my challenge, I admit, to thaw him into a little blond-haired prince.

Last night we toasted you, linking arms in front of the world chart in Father's study, with mugs held high. Where is our Charles at this very moment? We blew kisses north-east-south-west, hoping that, as the world turns, the winds will carry at least a few to you.

Your Catharine

WINTER, 1895

Sophie, it's a shame, but our world would be nearly perfect if it weren't populated by imperfect humans. What follows is a good illustration of that.

It's true that when Capt. Wilkes was in Europe stocking up for the voyage, he overlooked the purchase of microscopes. "I suppose that everything earthly, aerial, or aquatic, all the minutiae of the biological underbelly too small to be seen with the naked eye, was considered by our captain too insignificant to bother with!" one of the Expedition's scientists later noted. Fortunately, the omission was discovered and corrected before the fleet departed. It's also true that Wilkes was far more interested in charting land than in collecting samples and advancing the natural sciences. If the Scientifics came up short, nevertheless, he was quick to scold them. When two officers summited Sugar Loaf in Rio de Janeiro and failed to measure the mountain's altitude, he ordered them to repeat the climb the next day to fix the oversight.

The scientist who especially locked horns with Capt. Wilkes was our close family friend, Joseph Couthouy. The Boston-born conchologist's extraverted, impulsive nature stood in contrast to the captain's cautious, frequently paranoid behavior. A year or so into the voyage, their differences came to a head on a stopover at a mid-Pacific atoll. Couthouy was bringing aboard pieces of coral and storing them on the gun deck, when Wilkes summoned him and complained that Couthouy was overloading the ship. Wilkes thought the stench from the dying corals might cause malaria or other sickness in the crew.

From then on, Couthouy had to severely curtail the species he brought on board. No mollusks of any kind were allowed belowdecks. Restricted to the upper deck, exposed to the elements and lacking sufficient lighting, Couthouy found it nearly impossible to carry out the job of taking notes and labeling specimens.

"On my suggesting that previous expeditions had experienced no difficulty in the preservation of large and numerous specimens," he later recounted, "Capt. Wilkes replied that he did not care a damn for what had been done on previous expeditions."

Couthouy's one wish for the collection was that the Government would be proud of it and want to display it. But he was left with serious doubts this would happen.

To Charles Pickering aboard the USS Vincennes
From Catharine Pickering, Boston

February 2, 1839

Dearest Cousin,

The Society's Museum continues to accumulate samples at an alarming rate. As you once said yourself, it's every curator's dilemma. No one wants to turn away an interesting specimen, yet space is at a premium.

Part of the problem are self-appointed "naturalists," who are eager to contribute to our holdings and whose numbers are on the rise. I had to hide my amusement yesterday when Mrs. Willoughby crossed the threshold with a decomposing albino squirrel in a bag. I would have thought that playing whist with her lady friends was her favorite pastime, but she told me that when the weather is nice, there's nothing she'd rather do than take a walk in the woods with her dogs and her "trusty Winchester."

Just this week we've listed 200 new specimens. My favorite is a translucent blue-tailed lizard, the only known example found in New England. It was caught with great trouble in a mud hole in Vermont. Its tail really is the color of a penetrating August sky, crossed with yellow and black lines. Nature is such an accomplished artist, far better than we mortals!

We also received a fossil of an extinct fish sent by the esteemed Swiss biologist, Louis Agassiz. The Society elected Mr. Agassiz an honorary member last year, not without objections. He may be popular in Europe, but some of our members feel that his theory of ancient global ice sheets covering Europe is farfetched and too thinly demonstrated.[46]

Surprises never cease at L'Histoire. That's what James Cutting calls our establishment, L'Histoire—and it is a story, an on-going one. A dealer from Philadelphia brought in what he peddled as a new discovery, a pygmy bison that looks exactly like a full-grown male. Save for its height of 7 or 8 inches. It has a bison's shaggy head, its same forward hunch, and same horns, hoofs, and tail. Yet Mr. Harris has discovered that it's fabricated!—and the dealer has evaporated into thin air. Whoever made it was a capable craftsman & managed to cover a piece of wood with the skin of a pug-dog; the head, hair, and belly of an embryo bear; and a buffalo's black horn for horns and hoofs.[47] The piece is so remarkable, we've left it on display with this clarification: "Pygmy Bison, Art of a Hoaxster."

A quite different cry of foul is encircling the city. Jessie Willis and I attended *Merchants of Venice* at the Tremont the other night, and during intermission, the chatter in the lobby was about Dr. Charles Jackson, not the play.

As you know, Dr. Jackson has been one of our Natural History Society's staunchest supporters and most avid collectors. His minerals are among the Museum's prized objects, and he works tirelessly to add new samples. But last week he caught his colleagues off-guard when the *Boston Post* published a letter in which he emphatically stated that the invention of the electromagnetic telegraph is due mostly to his experiments, not those of Samuel Morse. He claims that when both men were returning from Europe on the packet ship *Sully* a few years ago, he discussed the details of his work with Mr. Morse, who, he asserts, professed his ignorance of the technology. Then, later, proceeded to make liberal use of the exchange. Mr. Morse is currently in Europe but certain to respond to Dr. Jackson's charges once he returns.

I wish you were here to lend your sound judgment. It's next to impossible to know where the truth lies.

February 12, 1839

Rev. Peabody and James Cutting met in the Library yesterday, principally to start an inventory of the shore birds in our cases. Their rapt study of each bird—how similar they are, the way they notice every remarkable feature.

Like the Reverend, Mr. Cutting is passionate about protecting wild birds from over-zealous hunters and has even started an organization. "Hunters Without Guns," he calls it. The two men met when Rev. Peabody joined the group. Members go on weekly walks for the sheer pleasure of encountering plants and animals. Guns are not permitted. Whereas, telescopes for observing species are strongly encouraged.

Mr. Cutting's own decision to stop carrying a gun came after a terrible accident, which he described in some detail.

"It was spring, and I was deep in the New Hampshire woods, when a sudden downpour soaked my powder. My gun was as useless as a wet mop, but there was nothing to be done, so I started for home. Just as suddenly the sun came out, and so did every creature I would have had in my scope. They seemed to be taunting me. A deer jumped the path. A large fox trotted next to me for a spell. A mob of grouse exploded out of a thicket. It was too frustrating for words. So, I decided to play a game. With each encounter, I took aim, pulled the useless trigger and cried 'Pow!' Normally I miss a lot—my shots hitting leaves or air. This new game was surprisingly satisfying, with each shot finding its mark. Or so I pretended.

"My pace slowed. Woodsy perfumes released by the rain had a drugging effect, and I drifted along in a pouch of peacefulness that was entirely new to me. Usually I'm too busy searching the sky or the undergrowth, too busy looking for the next target, I guess!

"Along the trail were flowers and ferns I normally ignored. Now I noticed their wild, bright designs. I knelt down to drink at Eden's Brook and watched in fascination as waterbugs skittered on the surface and fish grazed below. Then, looking up, I was transfixed by a sight upstream. A mother bear and her cubs were standing in the shallows, swatting the water for fish. First one plump trout, then another, sailed through the air. When a third jumped up, the mother batted it over the heads of the cubs, who went splooshing after it, grunting with delight.

"I'd known this forest since boyhood but I'd never seen it so animated. I'd always come with a gun, disrupting the quiet, drawing the life out of it."

Splooshing! Mr. Cutting likes to invent words as well as tools, it seems. Father might raise an eyebrow, but I expect he'd enjoy this young man's inventiveness.

"This perfect afternoon alone did not cure my hunting habit. But the events of the next day would. My cousin, Hugh, one of the finest men I'll ever know, his ten-year-old son Todd, and I went out to scare up some game. Todd was learning the protocol. In the case of sitting birds, better to shoot at the head if you planned to eat the torso. Better to use fine shot that tore the skin less if you planned to stuff it. For birds on the fly, aim several fingers ahead.

"Like boys his age, Todd did everything a little too fast. He walked too fast, he inspected the sky too fast. We entered a clearing and across the way, high up in a sturdy pine, sat a magnificent hawk, predator of the beloved quail. Each of us went through the motions, Todd included. He excitedly loaded his rifle and was taking a few eager steps forward, when a root snagged his boot, causing him to lurch forward. In one awful second his gun discharged. His father, also advancing, caught the bullet in his back, and sagged to the ground without a sound. I'll always believe Hugh stifled his cry for fear of frightening his son.

"My shot meanwhile found the hawk, which lay where it fell, its bill opening and closing, until I could no longer bear the sight and shot it dead.

"That was the last time I pulled a trigger. Two lives lost that day, a man and a bird of prey, all because of a miserable contraption made by humans. Birds of prey? You would have to agree, we are humans of prey! You can be sure the forest shuddered and muddered that night with a soulful elegy sung by the hawk's extensive family."

Mr. Cutting has ruddy cheeks and eyes the color of a summer sky. He's too fair to look grim, yet grim he looked just then.

February 28, 1839

I didn't feel well today and stayed indoors reading a book James Cutting loaned me. It was written by an "anti-hunter," as he calls himself. And expresses what James talked to us about—how hunters traipse through the woods, chiefly to kill, and fail to notice the life all around them.

Here's a small sampling: "I have known fox-hunters, who year after year have ranged all over the woods for miles and miles, and who never saw the biggest woodpecker that lives in them, the pileated. They have heard him calling them to come and see what a brave woodchopper he is, how he can make the chips fly and the woods echo to his strokes. But they had come hunting foxes, not woodpeckers, and had no time to turn out of their way to visit him, and he was too great a personage in woodpecker circles to come to them." [48]

The Reverend calls Mr. Cutting "a fellow of undoubted genius," and praises, above all, his empathy for animals. He can tuck himself inside their souls. View the world from their perspective. Know what they are thinking and feeling. Clearly, animals are as full of emotions as we are. I'm thinking of your mother's horse Flame, and how he gallops up to the fence whenever Lurena arrives—as smitten as the rest of Salem's gentlemen!

A few pieces of news. The Wendells had twin girls, a pattern on Eleanor's side. Also, a string of elderly has passed on, leaving me to wonder if New Englanders die more often in winter than in summer. Which would make perfect sense.

Andrew Lyman was one of those lost. He passed away suddenly one afternoon in the Society's library in his favorite chair, a newspaper on his lap. Mr. Chase, the librarian, distinctly heard him utter, "Oh Lydia, my love," before he slumped forward. No one thinks it wise to share his last words with his grieving wife Martha.

Finally, we expect your brother to announce his engagement to Charlotte any day. Lurena thinks they'll wait to wed until you're home. Then again, they are like two glow worms and may not be able to be that patient!

We long for your news, no letters having reached us yet. The papers run occasional updates about the Squadron—so at least we know your progress and presume you are safe & sound.

Catharine

Winter, 1895

Eventually it became all too noticeable. Shortly after someone reported an invention, always one of great significance, Dr. Jackson would rush to claim the idea as his own.

It happened with some regularity. In the 1830s, after U.S. Army surgeon William Beaumont zeroed in on the chemicals involved in digestion, Dr. Jackson insisted the original finding was his. The dispute with Samuel Morse over the telegraph came next and dragged on for years. Then, in 1845, after Christian Friedrich Schönbein announced his creation of guncotton, Dr. Jackson seized upon that as well. I actually remember, and quite clearly, the time he gave a demonstration at the Boston Society of Natural History in how to prepare guncotton, and his remarking how amazing it was that such a powerful explosive was derived from a substance as soft as the cotton-wool ladies wrap their valuables in.

Another controversy heated up in 1846. Dr. William Morton showed that inhaled sulphuric ether could cancel out the pain of surgery, only for Dr. Jackson to make the claim that he had given the idea to Dr. Morton, along with instructions for ether's application.

To be fair, Dr. Jackson, who gave up practicing medicine in order to examine the new natural sciences, was one of the first men of science to explore aspects of geology, mineralogy, and chemistry. He was an unstoppable virtuoso, the way he burrowed into these new disciplines. Educating younger scientists was high on his list, and he established a chemistry laboratory that, along with one in Philadelphia, was the first in the country. The quarrels he incited, however, undermined his reputation and, it would seem, his health. He spent his final years at the McLean Asylum for the Insane outside of Boston.

To Charles Pickering aboard the USS Vincennes
From Catharine Pickering, Boston

March 10, 1839

Our Cherished Charles,

Everywhere around Boston there's great excitement. Dr. Binney's pre-diction of an instrument that will surpass the camera obscura has come true. News has reached us from overseas of a device called a daguerreotype, after its French inventor, Monsieur Daguerre. An Englishman has produced a similar invention.[49] The process is compared to "drawing with sunlight." Solar light is the only active agent and fixes in place an image received through the camera's aperture, almost as if the picture makes itself!

The result is both miraculous and a little odd. Stationary people and objects are imprinted; moving ones aren't. So, in Monsieur Daguerre's picture of a boulevard in Paris, the stationary street, buildings and paving stones are shown in fine detail. But a multitude of pedestrians and carriages that were traveling up and down the street when the image was made are missing. The same is true of a man having his boots brushed. Only his legs are visible—they were stationary—while his upper torso is missing.

This is not a good method for portrait-making, since a sitter has to sit quietly for so long. But James thinks he can improve the process, speed it up. He's so sure of this, he has his sights set on opening a profitable portrait business downtown.

James lives in a modest bungalow beside Swallow Pond, and last Saturday, Rev. Peabody hitched up his horse and carriage, and off we sped to Brook-line for a visit. March has been typically erratic—one day sun, the next day rain. Thankfully we bundled up, because, sure enough, it snowed on the way home. James works in a lopsided barn beside the house, where you'd feel right at home.[50] Spears and fish lines, wagon wheels, saws and ice tools hang from the rafters. A crowded workbench stretches along one wall that sags so, it looks close to collapse.

One of his projects is a "practical" beehive. Practical, because growing up on a farm, he realized that most people, including his father, were ter-rible beekeepers. They were always upsetting their bees and got stung a lot, so James designed a hive with removable drawers that makes it possible to harvest the honeycomb without disturbing the bees.[51] He also is hard at work on a wooden snowplow that is so light, a horse can pull it as easily as a sled.

But it was an experiment off in a sunlit corner that especially caught our eye. Several weeks ago, James put a small fish in a glass jar with sea-lettuce and plugged the jar with a stopper. He never changes the water and only removes the stopper to feed the fish bits of meat once or twice a week. Yet the fish stays alive, he told us, because the sea-lettuce releases oxygen into the water. You would understand this alchemy better than I do. He has performed this experiment with both fresh and saltwater fish. Someday he wants to open a fish zoo right in Boston's downtown district.

In downtown? I asked, quite certain he must mean next to the wharves. He cleaned off two stools for us to sit on. Watching his face and its serious lines, I could tell that his idea wasn't only unorthodox but that he was highly invested in it.

"Yes! fish swimming on the same block as watchmakers, cobblers and bankers! Imagine stepping off a busy street and entering a large room where you can walk around looking at creatures normally hidden under ocean waves! Floozing flounders, scoozing moray eels, waving crabs, turtles and dolphins and silvery sharks!"

Not much seems to faze this young man. Sharks in downtown!

For the better part of an hour, he showed us various gadgets he has designed. A wooden clock, an elegant cigar lighter, a machine for breaking the husk off coffee berries, a double-handled saw for felling trees. Just before we left for home, he exhibited the handsome brass telescope he takes on walks into the countryside, self-made as well.

"So much happens now that I leave my gun at home.

"Yesterday, I was climbing Bear Hill when cries in the undergrowth led me to a large black snake coiled around a rabbit.[52] I killed the snake with a stone. The rabbit dashed off, unharmed, I think. I was curious to see the snake's last meal, so cut it open, and there lay fifteen quail eggs in its belly, all unbroken save for one. I'm not kidding. The broken one contained a tiny chick the size of a bumblebee, its tiny heart still beating, not to be saved. I was transferring the rest, using moss like gloves, to a nest of pine needles high in the crook of a tree, when a gray speckled shape came tearing out of the bushes, squawking and flapping. —The mother quail! She wasn't to be deterred by either human nor snake.

"Two days later I went back and, through my scope, I could see her on her eggs. A quail I once would have once shot and eaten. It was extraordinary.

Her new poults will make the forest a noisier and gladder place with their calls and flutters."

James Cutting is thoughtful to every kind of beast. He gave our horse some feed and made sure no stones were lodged in its shoes. On the carriage ride back to the city, the falling snow seemed warm and soft as fur.

March 19, 1839

You'll like this news. The Society's membership is approaching 200! Women, however, still cannot become members in their own right. This is especially hard on widows. I know two who would welcome using the reading room. I mentioned this to Dr. Binney, but a sneeze conveniently sent him running for a handkerchief.

There's a proposal afoot to advance Mr. Audubon from a corresponding to honorary member.[53] Since his Birds of America plates began to appear, Boston is more and more infatuated with the artist. He is a rare talent, there's no doubt. And yet some sides of Mr. Audubon aren't so admirable.[54] He made a gift to the Society of the wire model he used for his portrait of the golden eagle. It hangs at the head of the stairs, and whenever I pass beneath, I feel a rush of cold air. The eagle's awful death? Or the artist's ego? It could stem from either. I've heard how relentlessly the artist pursues his subjects. It's almost a ritual. He praises the bird flying overhead, its song, its plumage, its aerial grace. And then what does he do? He lifts his gun and fires!

Dr. Parkman saw this happen with his own eyes: One Louisiana morning, Mr. Audubon stood admiring, amid the smoke of earlier missed shots, a Mississippi Kite's desperate efforts to move her chick to a more distant tree. Yet, after a few moments, he still brought down mother and baby with a single shot. Pleased with his marksmanship!

"Keen is the desire of possession!" he told Dr. Parkman. He shoots as many birds as he likes, without restraint, creatures he calls his "soul-mates."

Dr. Parkman, as much as he admires Mr. Audubon, confesses that sometimes the artist goes too far. The strange episode that occurred a few years ago, in 1832, when Mr. Audubon, his wife and two sons were in Boston for the winter season—I wish Dr. Parkman hadn't told me about the golden eagle, and it must be why I feel such a chill when I pass beneath it.

It all began in the mountains of New Hampshire when a hunter set his spring trap, intending to capture a fox or two. When he returned, the trap was gone.[55] A careful search turned up the trap over a mile away, carried there in a surprising way. A large golden eagle, taking the bait, had gotten one of her talons caught in the trap and flew, carrying the trap, to a rocky crevice, where the trap had lodged tight. Despite the fatigue the bird must have been feeling, she wasn't easy to corner. Finally, she was secured, placed in a cage atop the hunter's wagon, and brought to Boston's Faneuil Hall market, where Mr. Greenwood saw the exquisite eagle and purchased her for his New England Museum.

A few days later, an errand brought Mr. Audubon to the Museum. One look at the eagle, who stood over three feet, and had a wingspan of seven feet, and the artist gave in to his addiction. He had to possess this magnificent creature. He paid Mr. Greenwood a fair price, took the bird home, and studied her from every angle. The eagle in turn regarded him with "looks of proud disdain." That's how Audubon describes the encounter in his Ornithological Biography, which is in our library now.

"At times I was half inclined to restore to him his freedom, that he might return to his native mountains." Cousin, the bird was in fact a *she*, but perhaps Audubon assumed only a male bird can have such exquisite plumage.

"I several times thought how pleasing it would be to see him spread out his wings and sail away towards the rocks of his wild haunts; but then, reader, someone seemed to whisper that I ought to take the portrait of the magnificent bird, and I abandoned the more generous design of setting him at liberty, for the express purpose of showing you his semblance."[56]

How like him!—to briefly wrestle with his conscience before deciding to kill the eagle, in the name of art. Once dead, the bird would be mounted on Audubon's system of wires, to replicate the bird's semblance of flight for the artist's drawing. He consulted Dr. Parkman. What fatal infliction would cause the bird the least amount of pain? The doctor offered a few suggestions. A subtle poison. Perhaps an electrical charge or suffocation. Opting for suffocation, Audubon placed the bird in a small room. Blankets were draped over its cage, the door and windows were sealed, and charcoal in a pan was lit.

Audubon, working in the next room, kept an ear out. He expected to hear a thump—the bird falling off its perch. The hall clock struck the hours, five in all, but there was not a sound. When at last he entered the room, the fumes were so strong, tears ran down his face. Yet, when he peered beneath the blanket, the eagle was sitting as regally as ever, her same "unflinching" eye directed toward her would-be assassin.

More hours went by. Another check at midnight revealed a still unchanged eagle, her eye still alert. A total of ten hours had passed, and by now the fumes were so strong throughout the apartment, the family spent an hour airing out their chambers until, exhausted, they fell into bed.

At dawn's first light, Audubon renewed his efforts, this time adding sulphur to the charcoal. The vapors were so noxious, the entire family felt queasy, and yet the eagle continued to sit tall on her perch and stared back defiantly whenever anyone checked on her.

Over the course of these mistrials, someone else might have caved in. The bird was so noble and stunning, it deserved to live. And no, it wasn't defiance in her eye, it was wisdom. Or bird-courage. Or maybe bird-pain or bird-sadness. But not Audubon, who was more determined than ever to finish the job, to possess the golden eagle and turn her into his masterpiece.

It's said that Audubon's stepmother, who raised him, gave in to his every wish. Is this why he is the way he is? Because he was spoiled as a child, and took and took? He developed a greedy heart, instead of a giving one?

It ended up that he resorted to a technique that never failed. He drove a thin steel needle through the eagle's heart. The bird was instantly dead without so much as a tremble.

Audubon worked obsessively on his drawing, as if to atone for murdering the bird. After he finished, he fell gravely ill, which is when Dr. Parkman was called for and returned him to health. You know the finished piece—the golden eagle soaring in flight, a bloody rabbit in her clutches. Does Audubon see the parallel between the artist, the eagle's assassin, and the eagle, the hare's assassin? I rather doubt it.

When I look at the painting, all I see is *torment*.

SPRING, 1895

Sophie, in Audubon's day the best way of studying a certain type of bird was, unfortunately, to kill it. Telescopes existed, but they weren't very portable; and binoculars wouldn't be in many hands until early the next century.

Catharine's disillusionment with Audubon, however, was understandable. His artistic genius hid from view his blind ambition and a handsome man's arrogance. Nature was there to entertain him, serve him, and relieve the boredom between hours. Indeed, it was a game to hunt game. And during his younger years, he and most everyone else believed wild species were unshakeable. When large flocks passed overhead, he would see how many birds he could bring down before missing one. He'd shoot seabirds from the deck of ships to work on his aim, despite not being able to retrieve them.

He once acknowledged that it was a rare day when he shot fewer than a hundred of those he referred to as "soul-mates."

To Charles Pickering aboard the USS Vincennes
From Catharine Pickering, Boston

May 7, 1839

Cherished Cousin,

Our friend Samuel Morse is still in Paris & hasn't yet replied to Dr. Jackson's charge—that he invented the telegraph, not Mr. Morse. Presumably he is preparing a response.

Meanwhile, the Boston Courier published a letter from Mr. Morse about an entirely different invention—the daguerreotype. He met with Daguerre in Paris a few months ago, and hails it as "one of the most beautiful discoveries of the age." The Frenchman, after his announcement, had no further plans to show his images until his government sealed its intent to acquire the rights for his discovery. Mr. Morse was eager to see them, however, and promised Daguerre a private demonstration of his telegraph in return.[57]

On March 7th, Mr. Morse visited Daguerre's office and residence at No. 5 rue des Marais, which lies next door to the theater where Monsieur Daguerre constructs and exhibits his dioramas that are so celebrated. Our friend was bowled over by the images he saw that day.

"You can hold a daguerreotype under a magnifying glass, and the tiny details actually increase. It's perfectly remarkable!" Mr. Morse remarked in his letter.

The very next day, Daguerre called on Mr. Morse at his apartment and was equally impressed by the telegraph's inner workings. As Mr. Morse tells it, the day was to turn disastrous for Daguerre. Later, when the Frenchman returned to the rue des Marais, he found his Diorama theater ablaze, with firemen scrambling to extinguish the flames.

Luckily, most of his papers, pictures and equipment were stored next door and escaped damage. But the theater and Daguerre's hand-painted dioramas were reduced to ash.[58]

May 27, 1839

Mr. Morse is finally back in New York and has wasted no time expressing his astonishment that Dr. Jackson is selling himself as the inventor of the telegraph. Here's an excerpt from his letter in yesterday's *Morning Post*:

"If further evidence were needed of the absurdity of Dr. Jackson's claim to my invention, it may be found in the correspondence he had with me on the subject in 1837, in which he pronounces the essential parts of my invention 'impracticable,' and proposes a mode of his own, not only bearing no resemblance to mine, but so awkward and complicated as to convince everyone who has read his letter that he could not have been the inventor of my Telegraph."[59]

The two men's exchange, excruciatingly public, grows more heated each day. Father wisely avoids siding with either friend. He noted at supper the other night that it wasn't that long ago when Dr. Jackson tried to take credit for insights connected to Dr. Beaumont's research into digestion. On the other hand, Father wonders at Mr. Morse's sudden proficiency in electronics, when up until recently his sole desire was to be an artist.

Meanwhile, the Frenchman's picture-making invention has taken Boston by storm! Dr. Binney, usually so reserved, was all but jumping up and down when he described Daguerre's trick of photographing a tiny spider at the annual meeting.

"*First*, he magnified its image with a solar microscope! *Next*, he set the image under a lens and took its picture. Normally you can barely make out a spider's parts. But photographed, they loom large![60] The spider's hairy legs, its multiple eyes, queer abdomen, and fangs—they all appear wolf-size!"

Dr. Binney called the new invention "an irrefutable god-send for science!"

Father sees it as "proof of Nature's existence."

May 30, 1839

This will make you cheer! Father has been elected President of the American Academy of Arts and Sciences, filling the position formerly occupied by Dr. Bowditch. His position as the city's Solicitor General stretches him thin. But you know Father; he couldn't say no. He meanwhile stays up half the night corresponding with his linguist friends overseas.

Your mother reports that seasickness has been a constant problem for the Expedition's sailors, and that several have had to abandon the cruise. And that you, also, have been leveled by *mal de mer*. I so sympathize. Mr. Darwin wrote in his diary how seasick he was on his *Beagle* voyage. It was a myth, he claims, that you ever get used to the waves. He swore that the only cure was to reach the next port.

We pray the fleet is safely past the dangerous Horn and making progress in a northerly direction. What I would give to be on Vincennes as you advance up South America's coastline, pause in those harbors, meet the natives and observe the wildlife—though seasickness would also strike me down and make me a hopeless companion!

Your loving Catharine

WINTER, 1895

Little Bear, when you look around, your eye doesn't catch them, because you've grown up using them. But mine does, all the recent inventions that take us somewhere without having to move a toe.

Mr. Morse actually confided to Uncle John Pickering that he'd been a nervous wreck about Monsieur Daguerre and his photographic method. He viewed the Frenchman as a rival, for there was no telling what governments might spend on the daguerreotype, which, like the telegraph, promised to facilitate the passage of information. Funds to establish his telegraph between cities might be depleted as a consequence. His meeting with Daguerre, however, put him at ease. As they talked, it became clear that their inventions could stand side by side. Neither inventor ran the risk of being overshadowed by the other.[61]

"Ah, Monsieur Daguerre," exclaimed Mr. Morse, "both inventions spring from natural forces. Yours from light. And mine"—his finger did a quick zigzag through the air—"from lightning," by which he meant the telegraph's use of electricity.

In hindsight, it was a curious coincidence that Daguerre's diorama business burned down when it did, because in a short time the Frenchman's daguerreotypes would become tremendously popular, while scenes painted on large canvases would never again be so interesting to the public.

For the longest time Uncle John had envisioned inventions that would "annihilate time and space." Inventions that might solve the global "connection problem."

"People will be able to leap great distances without leaving their parlors," he told anyone who cared to listen. Nobody knew what he was talking about. Then suddenly, up sprang both inventions, the telegraph and daguerreotype, debuting practically the same year.

Yet, in the late 1890s, neither invention yet operational, as the Wilkes Expedition rounded Cape Horn, worry hung in Boston drawing rooms like cigar smoke. The Horn's violent winds had shaken many ships to pieces, and often the only way a family knew, or guessed, a ship's tragic fate was when it failed to return to home port.

The slow ship-to-ship network eventually brought word that the Wilkes fleet had survived Cape Horn and begun the long climb north along Chile's wild coast, then Peru's. The Horne's notorious rough seas had taken all the *Relief*'s anchors. However, the fleet of six was intact. Or at least that was true until somewhere between Orange Harbor and Valparaiso when a different ship, the *Sea Gull*, became separated from the others and went missing. She and her crew were never seen again, presumably obliterated by a storm. Shaken and delayed by this hardscrabble loss, as well as bad weather, repairs, illness and other circumstances, the remaining five ships didn't reach Callao, the seaport west of Lima, until July.

From there, the diminished fleet slanted west into the rugged heart of the South Pacific, setting a course for a distant group of coral islands. Among them were the white sands of Clermont de Tonnere, Serle, the Disappointments and the enchanted island of Dog.

To Charles Pickering aboard the USS Vincennes
From Catharine Pickering, Boston

June 15, 1839

Dearest Charles,

I awoke early this morning and, wanting to surprise Mother with fresh catch, strolled down to the fish market. There was Dr. Storer, hard to miss in his yellow swallow-tailed coat and tall silk hat, rooting around the wharves by dawn's first light for new examples of fish types. He takes his role as the Society's curator of ichthyology very seriously. As he does his report for the Commonwealth on its resident fish. His friendly manner has won him friends along the wharves; many fishermen save samples for him. He brings them back to the Society, studies and preserves them, eats breakfast, and continues on his way to the Medical School, where his students are used to their teacher's rank smell.[62] In two years he has catalogued 90 of the 120 species thought to be common off our coast, which is admirable, for he confesses that when he began the project, he couldn't distinguish flounder from sole.[63] He also has managed to preserve every species of reptile in the State save for one!

Incidentally, in regard to your attempt to enlist him. He regrets not joining the Expedition, but he sees himself as landlocked, his every moment consumed with fish or medicine, medicine or fish!

He's becoming something of an expert on the subject of fish-based medicinals used by the Indians and reeled off several examples. "Ashes of teeth from dolphin and bonito mixed with honey, for a child's painful teething.[64] Ashes of sea-turtle mixed with bear's-grease, for the growth of hair. A bone from a cod's head pulverized and added to liquid, for a woman's heavy flow." I could feel myself blushing—but he's a doctor, after all. "Sea mussels, dried, pulverized and applied with oil for the soars of hemorrhoids and piles."

Older cures, he swears, often work better than newer ones.

I told Mother about running into Dr. Storer, and how we laughed! Not that we don't believe in the old cures. It was more the picture of Dr. Storer reciting them so earnestly, with wrapped fish under each arm and his cork-screw hair sticking out in every direction from under his hat. He is a cheerful, hard-working man, and if I make fun of him, it is with great affection.

June 25, 1839

Since last summer, Boston has been expecting the arrival of two giraffes from New York, both brought from Africa a year ago on a ship with a special tall cabin. One of them is finally here, but only for a fortnight. I took the children to see this unusual creature, which is in the company of a bontebok and dark-eyed gazelle, also never seen in this country. Each animal is riveting, the giraffe especially so—its long tapering neck and skin smooth as silk! I wouldn't hesitate setting all three beasts free if a savanna was nearby, for how can they possibly be happy living so far away from their native land?

"Look!" shrieked Abigail. "It's got a blue tongue. Is it a blueblood?"

Abigail asks astonishing questions.

Absolutely, I told her. Giraffes are kin to Boston's bluebloods. We are all related—you, me, giraffes, turtles, elephants, bears, the whole lot!

Oliver wanted to know if he was related to Cecil, his family's parrot.

With a quick flick of her head, Abigail tossed her long pigtail over her shoulder. "*You* and *Cecil* and *me* and *Sarah*, we're all cousins," she said very precisely.

The guard explained that the giraffe is the rarest of creatures. That it was hidden away in Africa for so long, people imagined it was a creation of fancy, like a unicorn or griffin. And that it got its long neck from reaching for foliage. I expected Oliver to object and tell his crocodile tale. I also was afraid he would take out his peashooter—he carries it everywhere—and take aim at the giraffe's tail. Yet much to my surprise he remained quiet and well-behaved.

Is our mischievous little cousin growing up? He did just turn thirteen.

June 26, 1839

What have you missed this spring? The May Day celebration on The Common was as colorful as ever. And we are still talking about two plays at the Tremont.

Your mother, brother and Charlotte joined us for a Saturday matinee of Dickens' *Nicholas Nickleby*.[65] The hall was crowded with children, and their rustlings and whispers made the lines hard to hear. Still, it was a stellar performance. One paper raved that Dickens himself would be hard pressed to find fault.

Then a few weeks later, Junius Brutus Booth returned and performed his famous *Edward III*.[66] You know how he loses himself in his roles. He certainly did that evening. It was all very entertaining—not exactly Shakespeare's intention! During a duel with Harry of Richmond, he chased Harry over the footlights, up one aisle, down the other aisle, round & round the stage, until two stagehands pounced on him and carted him off-stage.[67] A bloodcurdling scream let us know that Richard had been killed. I'm afraid that's when the audience laughed loudest.

Before the play, Mr. Booth's manager had locked the actor in his dressing room, in an effort to keep him sober. No such luck. The actor opened a window and summoned an errand boy, who delivered a pint of whiskey to his door, which he drank through a straw through the keyhole! He might still be the country's most respected tragedian, but people are concerned he's drinking himself to death.

June 30, 1839

James Cutting came for supper last night. Father, Mother, Uncle Octavius and Aunt Jane—they were all keen to meet him. His beehive is selling briskly, adding to his reputation as an inventor of promise. He's putting the finishing touches on a related design, a sideboard hive with a glass wall that allows bees and their honey-making to be watched from the parlor.[68] Mother and Father said they would consider one for the Salem house, but I think they were only being polite and will forget.

The night being warm & pleasant, after supper James and I went for a stroll. The day had worn me out and we nearly didn't go, but it was a fortunate thing we did. After visiting the swans in The Garden's lagoon, we crossed Beacon Street, inched our way along Charles Street, trading thoughts about the fine objects displayed in storefronts—Mr. Hawkins has a china cat in the window with ruby eyes, our favorite item, we decided—and then were making our way to the north end, when, as we passed the Littlefields' cellar window, a small lick of orange caught James' eye. He bounded up the front steps, roused William, and together they ran to the cellar and smothered the flame. The workshop stove pipe must have shifted just before we walked by, which sent a spark onto a pile of rags.

James wrapped his arm around my waist, almost protectively, as we walked on.

"A close call!" So close! How far might that flame have traveled if not checked?

This new friend with bright eyes and a shock of red hair—he's become a good companion while you're away. We attend plays and concerts, take long walks along the harbor, and even rode the train to Salem to visit family and friends. Which hasn't gone unnoticed. Mrs. Macomber and her circle have more to talk about than usual. I'm only too happy to inject a little intrigue into their midst, and I'd guess that their stitching is more exact because of it!

Remember grandfather's advice? "Follow your heart, not your head." I actually have no other choice since my head is in the clouds, nowhere to be found.

WINTER, 1895

Sophie, it's life's most common theme—dust to dust, molecules to molecules.

People came from miles around to view Dr. Storer's exceptional collection of fish and reptiles. It even included the skeleton of a spermaceti whale. Yet once Dr. Storer wasn't able to attend to the collection, it fell to ruin.

This may have been unavoidable back then. When the person responsible for building and caring for a cabinet departed, whoever took over often lacked sufficient interest and knowledge to maintain it with the same fatherly devotion. Altogether, it boggles the mind to think of how many early collections of earthly possessions were lost or irreparably damaged, whether by pests, decay, poor judgment and ignorance, fire, earthquakes or sheer neglect. Demons of destruction are ever at the ready to reduce organic specimens to their basic elements.

Dust to dust, molecules to molecules!

Catharine occasionally mentions her fatigue and not being herself. She was a self-effacing young woman who was more attentive to other people's afflictions—as well as wrongdoings heaped upon eagles and sea-serpents, as she soon relates—than her own problems, and for her to make the smallest mention of her lagging energy suggests her illness was already in possession. When her sister returned from Europe, Cath confided to Mary that sometimes she lacked the strength to take off her shoes at night and slept with them on.

Mary made her see the family doctor, and tests revealed an incurable blood disorder—a fatal anemia that, as it happens, is now curable.

Her letters to Charles make no direct mention of her illness. She probably didn't want to worry her faraway cousin or take space away from news she felt was more interesting. Someone pleasant had come into her life, and gradually she let her cousin know this, as she gradually grew closer to James. She must have struggled a great deal, wanting more than anything to live a normal life.

To Charles Pickering aboard the USS Vincennes
From Catharine Pickering, Boston

July 16, 1839

Dearest Charles,

The Society's bird collection goes on expanding but is plagued by problems. It now boasts roughly 75 mounted specimens, with another 400 skins stored away. Sadly, hundreds of others have been ravaged by insects and discarded.[69] The curators are experimenting with everything under the sun to stop the bugs. Mothballs to arsenic!

Dr. Binney tries to get the word out about which skins we have, which we still lack, yet donated duplicates are inevitable.

Yesterday, Wadsworth Cabot arrived with a mounted Red Owl he'd shot in a hollow oak near Fresh Pond, along with her two babies, a species the cabinet has held for some time.[70] Whenever I gaze at a bird that has been gunned down, a pain shoots through me. By nature of their wings, birds were meant to rise above the reach of humans. The easy game of pulling a trigger, what an unfair advantage. What if birds took aim and shot us? We never look at things the other way around. If we did, maybe we'd acquire the empathy we lack for animals.

You can see, I've adopted James' view on the subject. Or possibly my own uneasiness with guns and the slaughter of wildlife has always been there, waiting to be realized.

Mr. Cabot fancies himself quite the hunter, and it's evident that he regards each bird he bags as proof of his excellent marksmanship. He doesn't seem to care a whit about the birds themselves, their songs or plumage. A species' idiosyncrasies draw no remarks from him. When I told him that the collection already contains Red Owls, his face darkened, and he looked at me with those coal-black eyes. His samples were superior to those already in the cabinet, he insisted.

I spun out a little Deuteronomy. *If you encounter a bird's nest containing a mother sitting on eggs or with her young, you shall not take the mother with her young.*

His face grew darker, and he waved those claws. "That's ridiculous! Everyone knows that research methods require duplicates. The bird population is inexhaustible, *it's there for our taking!*"

Aside from the fact that the Society has owl duplicates, now, because of Mr. Cabot, Cambridge had lost another Red Owl family. Possibly several if the two chicks were to have brooded. Ah, cousin, here it is again, that misplaced sense of privilege, a blind arrogance. Odd, isn't it, that Mr. Cabot wholeheartedly accepts Nature as the work of a loving God, and yet he has no qualms about killing that heavenly work.

Fortunately, Dr. Binney entered the Hall just then. He responded to Mr. Cabot in a cordial yet firm manner. Indeed, the Society's collection had its Red Owls; but even if it didn't, our policy was not to accept a mother and her young. However, since Mr. Cabot had brought us the birds, Dr. Binney would attempt to find another museum that might welcome them. His diplomatic handling of the matter was admirable. Mr. Cabot is both an officer and donates large sums to the Society.

Mr. Cabot muttered something and was out the door, leaving behind the motionless cotton sack. I suspect that by afternoon, he was once more preying on creatures who don't fight back, and making a game of it along the lines of hide-and-seek.

July 22, 1839

Dr. Storer shared a Troc'ulus about a phenomenon you're likely familiar with.

Years ago, clam fishermen discovered that starfish have a great appetite for clams. Off their piers when the tide was low, they would spy starfish prying open clam with their suckers. This was a remarkable finding, that starfish were competing with them. So the fishermen took to stripping the legs off starfish and cutting them into pieces, meaning to destroy them. Yet the population didn't diminish. In fact, the numbers of starfish seemed more plentiful than ever. Eventually it was discovered that they don't die when their legs are stripped, because they regrow them, and that they can even regenerate an entire body from a single detached arm.

The other day Father told me about a certain French snail that can regrow its entire head. "Voltaire knew about this snail, and was confident that humans would someday master the same skill. It would be a great help, especially for those with swelled heads," said father with a chuckle.

"Like Mr. Cabot!" I let slip.

Father, always diplomatic, said nothing though his smile gave him away.

I spoke too soon in respect to Ollie. Yesterday in church, Mrs. Hornblower let out a terrible scream and jumped so high, the Devil might have been rising up through the floorboards. A large black spider clung to her shoulder. Mr. Hornblower brushed the critter off his wife and promptly stomped on it. Ollie was sitting with his parents in the adjoining pew, looking like a little cherub. His timing was perfect, I must say. Rev. Broadlawn had been working up to a thundering climax, the veins on his neck standing out like blue rivers, when Mrs. Hornblower's screech deflated his sermon like a dam bursting.

James has given me the most beautiful writing desk which he carved himself. It has cubbyholes for papers and inks, and vertical panels that slide open to reveal hidden compartments. He said they were for letters.

Letters? from whom? I asked.

"Why me, of course, your most admiricious, razzaricious, sappillimonious admirer."

I don't usually blush, yet could feel my face heating like an iron!

And now he writes to me almost every day, even on days when we see each other. I'm glad to have these compartments. Mother is as curious as a cat about my comings and goings, and has been dusting my room unnecessarily. You would think she'd be glad one of her daughters has a gentleman friend. But I can tell she's mortified that the gentleman is so much younger, and mortified of what her friends might think.

If you were here, you would be winking at me across the dinner table, making light of it all and making me feel better.

With unwavering affection, Cath

WINTER, 1895

Sophie, I'm slipping in a letter that Charles sent from Peru around this time, the summer of 1839. It was the first letter the John Pickering family had received from him since the Fleet's departure the previous August, and it's covered with the thumbprints of countless people who read it. I've omitted some portions, for it runs long, but you'll find the letter stored with the others in the old table. He provides quite a harrowing Troc'ulus, as you'll see. The botanist Asa Gray liked to exaggerate the account, making it seem as though a Condor nearly was the end of his friend.

U.S. Ship Vincennes, Callao. July 12th 1839[71]

> Your letter of the 16th Dec. met me at Valparaiso, and I was most grateful. At the time, it was the only letter from home I had yet received. Since then, one other has arrived, but I can get no tidings of those sent through the Navy Department—I begin to lose faith in the Department, for it seems to know less about the movement of its own chickens than everybody else.
>
> Since our exploration of this continent began, I find myself in a state of almost constant turmoil and excitement, and have visited more places and seen more sights than I ever expected to on this voyage.
>
> Here in the harbour of Callao, we are surprised at the variety and numbers of sea-birds constantly about us. They are apparently attracted by the abundance of fish, and especially by the shoals of Anchovies. On the South side of San Lorenzo, we found the breeding places of some of these species, which occupy some inaccessible cliffs. Each species seemed to have a district or village marked out for itself.
>
> Most spectacular of all is the Condor, which no one in our own country has ever seen, at least not alive. My esteemed colleague Thomas Nuttall believes it to be a bird of North America, but I feel the evidence is missing. Messrs. Lewis and Clark obtained a bill

and single quill-feather credited to this large bird, but those remains better fit the California vulture, which also is a large bird. We first observed the Condor in the higher valleys of the Cordilleras, its proper home, and where it seems the bold fearless bird described by writers. I afterwards repeatedly observed it among the Amancaes mountains near Lima & along the sea-shore; and on one occasion saw as many as twenty perched on the ground a few miles from Lima. (The inhabitants say that the Condor feeds only on recently dead animals.) The flight or rather sailing of the Condor is exceedingly majestic, always slow, and sometimes progression is scarcely perceptible. The bird is perfectly motionless, unless it should happen to turn its head, or incline its tail in changing its course. In this manner it proceeds slowly down the valleys, often within a short distance of the ground. At times, however, it soars to a great height.

I have never seen the Condor flap its wings except on rising from the ground. And my observations of these birds at this point have been extensive, and within close range—on one occasion in May, too close, as I shall briefly recount. Several of us, both naturalists and artists, made an excursion from Callao to Banos, which is in the Andes and at the limit of Cultivation, with a couple of dozen scattered houses and a church. The ravine in which it is situated is very narrow & its border immensely elevated, rugged, and so steep that one of our party asked very innocently "why the Cattle did not fall off."

Having determined to remain there for the day, we separated into two parties. Messrs. Rich & Agate directed their steps down the stream, while Mr. Breckenridge and myself took the opposite direction. We ascended a good distance on the heights to the left, and met with great success in collecting plants, but Mr. B. being rather unwell did not wish to go to the summit & returned to lower ground. I continued ascending leisurely, collecting along the way, the acclivity gradually becoming steeper. By noon I had reached a very considerable elevation. About this time I observed a Condor coming down the valley, sailing slowly & majestically, & I stopped to observe its motions. To my surprise it took a turn round me, then a second & a third, the last time drawing so near that I began to think that the bird seriously meditated an attack.

I was in the worst humour possible for a fight—my strength was exhausted by climbing & my right hand was useless due to an earlier accident. But there was nothing to be done, so I took a seat & produced my knife. At that instant, as if acquainted with the iron, the bird wheeled off in a different direction; and I confess, however humiliating the acknowledgement, that I was at that time very well satisfied with his determination.

I think of home more often than you may suppose. Don't forget to make a regular memorandum of every event that happens; nothing is so unpleasant as returning home after a long absence with an uncertainty as to what has transpired in the meanwhile.

Your affectionate cousin Charles Pickering.

To Charles Pickering aboard the USS Vincennes
From Catharine Pickering, Boston

August 24, 1839

Dearest Charles,

I have pulled my writing desk closer to the open window where a hint of a breeze stirs. Mr. Crawford claims the water in his horse trough boiled yesterday. The temperatures have been so fierce, I believe him!

The heat has not stifled the excitement of last Sunday—perhaps added to it. As usual, the slowness of our correspondence across oceans makes me impatient, and I wish there was a speedier conduit for this news, so we might share it more or less at the same time. As it were, how can we smell the same smell separated by such a great distance?

On Sunday, Capt. Waterman ferried Mother, Father, Mary and me over to Nahant to celebrate the Winthrops' long marriage at a party held at the hotel. Roughly one-hundred guests attended and everyone wore white as requested, except for the Peabodys, who mistakenly wore black. They must have roasted. We had just finished a lavish dinner—many of us were seated on the front veranda and along the seawall—when a cry went up to look seaward. Something extraordinary was in progress. The calm ocean had turned tumultuous due to shoals of small fish rushing toward the rocks, apparently pursued by a shark. But no, it wasn't a shark! We saw features that were more snake than fish, and suddenly we were all shouting the same words at once—*sea-serpent!*—brethren of the serpents that have taken up residence in our community's collective memory after decades of reports of similar sightings in our section of the Atlantic. As if it heard us, the creature made a sharp turn back out to sea, and we were left staring after its remarkably long wake—or was that its tail?

Was it the famous serpent of the summer of '17, back for a visit? Dr. Binney and others speculated it well could be. It was just as long, but how long?

I've since read the Linnaean Society's report describing the 1817 sightings. Several people swore on a Bible they saw a serpent of large dimensions inside Gloucester Harbor and off Cape Ann, and most agreed it carried its head one or two feet above the surface, and that it was of a dark color—ostensibly dark brown. Otherwise, there was little agreement among the witnesses. The serpent had the head of a sea turtle. No, it resembled the head of a horse! Its length was roughly 50 feet. No, it was well over 100 feet! Its body was segmented, a "string of buoys." No, it was as smooth as a log! It was as wide as a barrel. No, half as wide!

This Sunday's serpent also caused a jumble of opposing viewpoints. The creature swam at the rate of a mile a minute. No, its speed was twice that! Some saw a hooded black eye; others didn't recall an eye. Gwinn Hovey maintains that the beast had a forked tongue that extended a good two feet. Albie Goodhue recalls ears.

It's hard to believe that anyone observed the serpent with total clarity. It came and went so quickly. We were stunned speechless. A mythical monster moving swiftly toward the promontory and then veering out to sea was hard to process. How comical we nubs of humans must have looked, gadding about in our bonnets and top hats on the terrace of a rather ugly box of a hotel. If the monster took any notice. James was right, though. Had a sea-serpent wanted to convince us that its type still occupies these waters, it couldn't have chosen a better time to parade by, so many of Boston's highbrows were present and left gapping after the monster.

Dr. Binney plans to write down everything just as he saw it. Sunday's serpent won't be forgotten.[72]

If there'd been a scintilla of doubt about what we saw—there wasn't, but if there had been—the scene at the Nahant Hotel was repeated the next day. The unerring Mrs. Grattan, the wife of the newly appointed British consul, was staying at the hotel for a week but missed Sunday's excitement due to a daytrip to

Providence. She was reading on the upper piazza when suddenly someone cried out, "Serpent!" Guests had been pretending to see the monster all morning, so at first she assumed this was more "wolf! wolf!" Yet, when she looked up, the serpent really was streaming past the seawall in front of her in a westerly direction! She said it was over 100 feet in length and advanced far faster than a whale.

Dr. Storer notes that reports of large sea Snakes off Norway's coast have circulated for centuries. So many centuries, that when Norwegian fishermen are asked by outsiders if such creatures are real, they roll their eyes and ask, 'Are cod and mackerel real?' Still, Dr. Storer suspects the Norwegians exaggerate the "serpent nonsense" to scare off other countries from straying into their fishing grounds.

He fully believes serpents once inhabited the oceans and that some may still be around. All the hoopla over their existence could be laid to rest, he said, if only a fossil or two were found as evidence. Is that true? None have been found? Anywhere?

How sad that the 1817 creature was fired on by passing ships, when it was simply lolling around & causing no harm. Here's a perfect example of firearms going beyond their intended use. Father said that a century ago, sailors saw a massive serpent coiled on a rock off Cape Ann. They were readying their muskets, when two Indians on board persuaded them to hold their fire. If they merely wounded the serpent, it might attack the ship! More importantly, it was bad luck to kill a creature from the ocean depths, they persuaded the captain. The sea gods had put it there for a reason.[73]

Nature continues to have her reasons, for every species!

Which reminds me. I found these lines written on a scrap of paper in Grandfather's desk. Any idea as to their origin? The handwriting is not the Colonel's.

> *We that never can make it,*
> *Yet dare to unmake it,*
> *Dare take it and break it and throw it away.*[74]

August 29, 1839

This Troc'ulus comes from an operator of a dry goods store in Derry who often contributes minerals for the collection. Coincidentally, the bird he speaks of might be a Troc'ulus, although he can't identify it so narrowly.

Last year Mr. Hale was at his wits' end. The noise from the swallows living in the chimney of his store had become so loud, two people could scarcely have a conversation. He imagined over one-hundred birds were roosting there, and the vibration of their wings sometimes sounded like rolling thunder. Moved to action, he made an opening in the lower part of the chimney into the counting room, and then his son climbed up a ladder onto the roof and lowered a thick board down the chimney. Luckily the family was standing outside, because a great gust of 256 swallows came whirling down into the counting room, way more than expected.

The next morning, his son lowered the board a second time, forcing out another 119. All 375 were placed in boxes with openings for air, then transported and released in the cornfields of a farmer who was ecstatic to be the recipient of so many swallows. The birds reliably perform the service of ridding his fields of insects while leaving the crops untouched.

The residents of Derry consider swallows "gifts from God." Mr. Hale thinks it's "impolitic and cruel" to destroy them and says that if it weren't for their handiwork, there wouldn't be a harvest.

Amen to that!

SPRING, 1895

Sophie, our ancestors understood how important birds and insects were for a successful growing season. No year taught them better than 1749, when tactics by Massachusetts' farmers backfired. A reward was posted for purple grackles and crow blackbirds—three pence per dozen—because the birds were feasting so voraciously on farmers' crops. Hunters turned out in droves and had a field day, shooting down the targeted species as well as curlew, plover, quail, prairie chicken and others. Then it was the insects who had a field day. With no birds to keep them in check, they ruined the grass and grain crops to such an extent that the colonists had to swallow their pride and ask England for hay for their cattle.

It's a lesson we can't seem to learn. Nature should be left to her own devices, find her own balance.

About Catharine's sighting of a large sea-serpent, similar stories have circulated for centuries, and I've never doubted their claims. Some people, however, speculated that these sea snakes emerged from the polar rivers of Captain Symmes' Inner World. If sea-serpents lived *down there*, the thinking went, they must occasionally escape *up here*, riding a strong current or losing their way. But that thinking went too far. Those claims were generally doubted by sea captains who otherwise accepted that the oceans were home to many monster species.

It's just too bad that sea monsters went into decline before the camera could document them. It's also unfortunate that no credible fossils have come to light, only trumped-up ones. In 1844, the skeleton of a 114-foot-long sea-serpent exhibited by a New York exhibitor became the city's most popular attraction, that is until Professor Wyman, a curator at The Boston Society of Natural History, examined it and revealed a hoax! The vertebrae were cemented together and came from different animals. Some of the vertebrae weren't bone at all, but casts made from the cavities of shells.[75]

To Charles Pickering aboard the USS Vincennes
From Catharine Pickering, Boston

October-November 1839

Dearest cousin,

I'm convinced Old Man Time is rudely stealing hours, the day just vanishes. Where does he hide them—in the folds of a cloud, in the blackness of night?—so that I might steal them back. My long pauses between letters otherwise have the excuse that I spend numerous hours at the Natural History Society; and with James Cutting, too. But I also tire easily and spend afternoons listless on my chaise with a book, and suddenly the day is as spent as I am.

A natural catastrophe surprised the Town of Gloucester a few mornings ago. Its residents awoke to find the great cove at the extremity of Cape Ann, its rocks and beaches, littered with dead pigeons.[76] It seems a large flock of these birds failed to start for their wintering grounds soon enough and were overwhelmed by a powerful nor'easter that did tremendous damage to many fishing boats in local harbors. Neither human—nor bird apparently—expected the storm to be so severe.

If you were here, you would undoubtedly enter into the pigeon debate that is raging. James, Rev. Peabody and others hold the opinion that New

England's wild pigeons are declining, and quite rapidly, whereas, were you to ask Wadsworth Cabot, he would say the reduction is not significant and likely due to cataclysmic events like the recent gale. He also uses the example of the atmospheric disturbance over the Gulf of Mexico last spring that left those waters thick with dead pigeons.

"Oh fie," says Rev. Peabody, who contends that the fall-off in wild pigeons is so widespread that a fair number of hunters have noticed and commented on the change. "The weather isn't to blame. The market gunners are, and their scheming ways. Nets, flame, smoke, guns, even canons. God help the birds! Our felling of forests is a second evil. No woodlands, no pigeons!"[77]

Then he told me this awful story:

"Last spring, I had the misfortune of observing the most despicable deceit of all. I was in Essex County tracking information for my survey when I met an old man who claimed to have figured out a way of taking lots of pigeons all at once, a method that worked better than using a net and caused them little discomfort. He suggested I visit him the next day and see for myself.

"It was May and the birds were returning. I couldn't help wonder what trick the old codger had up his sleeve, so the next morning, right after sunrise, I went to his cottage, where he had built a pole pen out back. After he scattered ample wheat inside the enclosure, we took cover. The pigeons weren't long in coming. Streaming down, they pecked up the wheat ravenously, but as soon as they began stuffing themselves, their behavior turned strange. They began staggering and trembling, falling and struggling to right themselves, then falling and quaking and unable to stand. It turned my stomach to watch them; it seemed the old man must have poisoned them. At least one-hundred birds lay on the ground for easy bagging.

"The fox revealed his secret sauce—whiskey-soaked wheat! Better than poison, but still! the birds are doomed every time. It's the same old unbalanced contest of conniving human against innocent creature, and my emotions tugged at me just as if he had poisoned them, which is essentially what he had done." Rev. Peabody's eyes glistened with tears that cupped in the corners of his eyes.

Western states report millions of wild pigeon still pass overhead. But how long can they prevail? The female usually lays just one egg at a time. *One egg*, the Reverend emphasized. "The species is sinking faster than it can rebound, especially now that Boston and other cities are acquiring a taste for squab. The new rails encourage the slaughter. Transportation equals *sales* equals *profit*."

The birds Mr. Hodgkin sells sometimes come from as far away as Cheyenne. Cousin, tell me, shouldn't there be laws that protect pigeons, at least the squabs, the egg-bearers? Shouldn't state officials do more to limit gun sales and stop trigger-happy shooters?

More consequences! A boy of eleven in a town in western Massachusetts picked up a gun leaning in the corner of his home & pretended that he was going to shoot his young brother. He thought the gun was empty— and now the family is inconsolable! The father kept the gun loaded and at-the-ready to shoot pigeons flying overhead for a quick dinner.[78] Dead pigeons, and now a dead young son.

James worries that Americans have become so addicted to their guns, we've lost sight of what it means to kill. That's a frightening thought. It's some consolation that James' "No Guns" club is growing rapidly. Your friend Philip Harrington is a convert and has begun a chapter in Rhode Island.

November 3, 1839

This week, the cabinet acquired the skeleton of an earth pig found by Dutch colonists; a whale's cranium delivered by a captain and crew; and 40 African butterflies brought in by Lucy Pratt. She and her husband are often overseas, and Lucy always returns laden with unusual objects. And stories! She entertained us with this especially ludicrous tale, which occurred last spring on the outskirts of London.[79]

An English acquaintance of the Pratts purchased an enormous piece of meat from his local shopkeeper. It was a bear's ham with the foot still attached. The portion was so large, he decided to share the foot and sent it to a friend. Let's call him Friend #1. This friend couldn't make use of it, so he sent it on to Friend #2. Friend #2 was perplexed when he opened the package, as Friend #1's note of explanation, sent separately, hadn't arrived, and also because the foot had begun to wither and was not easily identifiable. Friend #2 therefore sent it on to Friend #3, a man of science, for identification, which Friend #2 thought was the reason that Friend #1 had sent it to him in the first place. The scientist decided the foot belonged to *a savage of unknown origins.* The more it had dried and shrunk, the more human it looked.

For another opinion, Friend #3 sent the wizened object to Friend #4, an anthropologist. Again, an explanatory note, sent separately, was delayed. By then, the package's contents presented such a ghoulish sight, the anthropologist summoned the police inspector, who had just learned of a murder. The foot, he decided, must belong to the poor murdered bloke whose family had buried him the day before. Friends #2 and #3 received their letters, explanations fell into place, and the disinterment that had been requested was halted. Otherwise, the police would have discovered that the decapitated victim still possessed both his ham and his foot.

Spring, 1895

You see, Sophie, the telegraph and the pigeon were on a collision course. The gun was the fatal blow, but the hunters knew where to go because wired messages informed them where pigeons were roosting and what direction they were flying in. The great food markets of Boston were becoming famous. The city's market-men were celebrated for their stocks of crustaceans, fish, poultry and wild game, and pigeon was a rising favorite, locally fledged pigeon as well as pigeon trapped and transported great distances by rail.

Technology! So helpful to humans yet so detrimental to wildlife.

The more trees were felled for farmland, roads, towns and commons, the more pigeons suffered, the more habitat was lost. In Massachusetts, the last significant nesting of pigeons is thought to have occurred in the year 1850. We descendants are beginning to admit that our forefathers stole land from the natives. But no one thinks to mention the woodlands that humans have so savagely wrenched away from wildlife.

To Charles Pickering aboard the USS Vincennes
From Catharine Pickering, Boston

January 10, 1840

Dearest Cousin,

May the ocean you sail over be the opposite in temperament to the cold, harsh Atlantic this December. Three terrific gales within fourteen days have taken the lives of scores of New Englanders, wrecked more than 90 vessels, dismasted another 200, and caused indescribable damage to piers, wharves, and other structures. Often too little remains of a ship "to judge who or what she was," one newsman writes. Bodies are still being recovered up and down the coast. You are acquainted with several of the deceased, but rest assured, our family came through unscathed. Your mother is safe & sound, and has had one gallant man after another checking on her. In the midst of one tempest, the great pine behind your house toppled with a great crash, at least missing the stables, and only spooking the horses, but demolishing the fence. Believe me, her admirers will rebuild it in no time!

On to brighter news, quite literally. Mr. Daguerre's photographic method is gaining popularity, but not for portraits, since a sitter has to sit still for so long. Samuel Morse posed his wife for twenty minutes, and still got poor results. John William Draper in New York, however, has sped up the process. He's taken the first picture of a human face lit by sunlight in a mere 65 seconds—of his sister in a becoming bonnet.[80] This new art shows every imperfection. Not that Miss Draper need worry; she looks at us with a kind expression of someone you'd like to meet. Will photographs draw us to certain people? And make us suspicious of others?

Father thinks images of loved ones will end up on every dresser, maybe in every pocket. I'm enclosing a pamphlet about Photogenic Drawing. James can help you master it once you're back. His experiments with photography are leaping along. His workbench is awash in chemicals that can make a face appear on blank paper. It's pretty strange, actually!

His experiments with bees also continue. He moved them inside for the winter and made the discovery that if he fastens a dead queen to the interior of the hive, the other bees keep working as diligently as if the Queen were alive. But as soon as he removes the dead queen from the hive, their work ceases.[81] We got laughing over what would happen to the country if a dead President was left sitting at his desk!

Because of James, I find myself scrutinizing Nature far more that I used to. The puzzles and innuendoes! Every bug might look like a funny foreigner but every bug is an essential part of our world. How dull our lives would be, James reminds me, without Nature's quintabillinimous mysteries!

Oh the words he comes up with! It was something his grandfather taught him, to say whatever rolls off his tongue!

Yes, I have an inner smile these days.

Your loving cousin Catharine

SPRING, 1895

Sophie, I have in my possession a letter, found in Uncle John's papers, that Charles wrote Cath in August 1840, sent from Fiji. A portion of it is copied below. He thanks her for the pamphlet on photography and imagines she'll think his letter "strange," because of his descriptions of the bizarre culture he finds himself in.

Fiji's natives, as much as they and their differences from European stock repelled Charles, fascinated him. Keep in mind, exploring the races of man was a completely novel concept, and our cousin was one of the first scientists to do the work of an anthropologist. (He covered so many disciplines, what was one more!) He and his uncle, John Pickering the linguist, were instrumental in persuading the Navy that the Wilkes Expedition was a golden opportunity to study relics from diverse cultures. The Scientifics sent home 1,202 objects from Fiji alone, and you can be sure that many were selected by Charles for their cultural aspects.

U.S. Ship Vincennes, Feejee Islands, Aug 8th 1840[82]

> Dear Cath,
>
> If I had been called upon to name a spot where I least expected to hear from home, I might possibly have mentioned this horrible place. Thank you for remembering me. Mother's letter has also come to hand. These are now all I have received since leaving Valparaiso. The missing letters I hope to find at the Sandwich Islands.
>
> I am much indebted for the pamphlet on Photogenic Drawing. I have myself sometimes thought of the possibility of such a thing.

While we have aboard the camera lucida, we sailed too soon to avail ourselves of those more advanced inventions.[83] It would be worth something, to bring home a true representation of some of the scenes we have witnessed among these people.

A person with knowledge of the worse scenes of the French Revolution might suppose he had seen something, but he knows nothing of human nature unless he has been among the Feejees! What are we to call these people? they are not savages, for they live in towns, some of one or more thousand inhabitants. In all that relates to the cultivation of the soil, they are great adepts. They wear wigs! & the time, labour and ingenuity they expend in the art of hairdressing is altogether beyond our ideas. They have musical instruments and are proficient in various departments of the culinary art. They are excellent navigators, and ingenious in various arts and manufactures.

And yet, these islanders prove that what so many of the most eminent men of the world say, that cannibalism exists nowhere in the world, is a lie. The Feejees do not kill their next-door neighbours for the purpose; yet a man dare not go alone to a neighboring village.

Here, people have their reasons for everything. They even have a reason, and a method, for preventing old age, a very simple but very effectual process, which I will describe, as I believe you would like to know the truth. For instance, when a son thinks his mother has lived long enough—maybe she is no longer able to bring down 200lbs of yams on her back from the mountains; or he may have got into a fret about something; or he may be tired of seeing her about!—he digs a hole at some distance and tells her that he is going to kill her! The old lady replies, "well my son, if I am no longer of any use, I had better be dead," & goes out with her son to the spot; for it would be very undignified to put him to the trouble of carrying her body. When he arrives, she stoops down and the ceremony is performed with a club. The son returns to the house, without any more apparent emotion than if he had been slaying a pig, & maybe in a month will hardly recollect it....

We have been here three months, which is two-thirds too long.

To Charles Pickering aboard the USS Vincennes
From Catharine Pickering, Boston

February 16, 1840

Fondest cousin,

Reverend James Clarke dined with us last Thursday, home once again after five years of ministering in Louisville.[84] His trials and tribulations were painful to hear about. The indifference he encountered among Louisville churchgoers made him reach out instead to the slaves of Kentucky, who ended up his heart's true flock. Their day of freedom is coming soon, he swears this is true.

He talked into the wee hours. Mother, Father, Mary and I fell under the spell of his cavernous voice as he recalled several unusual encounters he had in the South, none stranger than the evening he spent with Mr. Booth, the actor— the senior, mercurial, always-entertaining Booth whose mad gallop around the stage of the Tremont we witnessed last spring. The more I know about this illustrious tragedian, the more I begin to understand his own private hell, as he must suffer terribly for his uncommon ability to recognize what no one else can see. *They* call him insane. He thinks *they* are. Since I detest the same behavior he detests, which Rev. Clarke's story amplified, I can only think that no one is saner or braver than Mr. Junius Brutus Booth.

This is what Rev. Clarke recounted. He'd been in Louisville long enough to be discouraged by the apathy of his parishioners and his own inexperience as a young pastor, when one night there was a knock on the door of his cottage. It was a young boy with a note from a guest at the hotel. Rev. Clarke carries it still in his billfold and showed us:

United States Hotel, January 4, 1834

Sir,—I hope you will excuse the liberty of a complete stranger seeking you out. It is to inquire about a place of interment for his friend/s in the church-yard and also the expense of purchasing such a place of repose. Your communication on this matter will be tremendously helpful, sir.

Your respectful and obedient servant, J.B. Booth.[85]

To inquire about the availability of a burial lot, Rev. Clarke went in search of first one, then another, city official. Neither was home, so he walked to the hotel, where he asked to see Mr. Booth. Waiting in the lobby, he scanned the note in his pocket, and for the first time noticed that perhaps there was an "s" on "friend." "Friends"—? The writing was messy, and he couldn't quite tell. It must be an ink blot. Surely Mr. Booth wasn't intending to bury more than one friend. After a short wait, he was shown to a dimly lit parlor where a short man with an animated, edgy manner was seated with a pale thin gentleman who wore a patch over one eye. The first stood up, and Rev. Clarke immediately recognized the famous actor Junius Brutus Booth, whom he'd seen in a variety of roles.

He explained that he didn't yet have answers for Mr. Booth. Mr. Booth, in return, suggested he join them for a cup of brew. The Reverend thought that since the actor had lost someone close to him, he might be in need of a minister's support and consolation, and took a seat. For the rest of the evening, the conversation stayed between the two of them, the third gentleman never uttering a word. He may have been intimidated by the actor, who was extremely animated that evening. Or perhaps, Rev. Clarke decided, he was a ghost! He couldn't catch the individual's one uncovered eye, or even see into it, the candlelit room was so dark.

The Reverend kept bringing up Mr. Booth's loss but got nowhere.

When did his friend die? —"Recently, very recently."

Was it a long illness? —"No, it happened suddenly, very suddenly."

Was he or she a relative? —"Distant. But, yes, a relative."

As if to change the subject, Mr. Booth pulled a book out of his satchel and asked the Reverend if he would like to hear Coleridge's "Ancient Mariner." The Reverend would be delighted. Ever so quickly, the actor transformed into the mariner and spun the poem's mystic layers so tightly, that when he ended, it was a struggle for the Reverend to mentally return to the dimly-lit parlor where across from him sat the half-blind ghost and the actor with frenzied eyes.

Mr. Booth's volume also contained poems by Shelley. Was the Reverend familiar with the passage in 'Queen Mab' that decries using animals for food? Yes, Rev. Clarke knew the lines Mr. Booth was referring to. What was the Reverend's opinion of such sentiments? Rev. Clarke replied that he respected them but was not inclined to adopt them.

"Ah, but I did, and many years ago," said Mr. Booth. "I believe wholeheartedly that it's wrong to kill an animal for our pleasure and to serve it at our supper table. I eat from the garden, or, as tonight, I'm satisfied with a loaf of bread. The Bible supports this view."

He asked for a Bible, and once the waiter brought it, he thumbed through it so capably, picking out and reciting passages from Genesis to Revelation, that he must have read the selections many times over. They built the case that, until the Deluge, humans originally ate grain legumes, such as beans and lentils. Only after the Deluge, because of their disillusionment, did they turn to killing animals, for meat as well as for sport.

By then, said Mr. Booth, humans had forgotten what life was like in Eden. Their hearts had hardened; they had lost the memory of when they were one of many animals within God's fold. They had forgotten their love for their fellow creatures, their oneness with them. They had forgotten, and consequently they had turned empty and uppity.

Mr. Booth's eyes were welling with tears. He rose, fetched a candle from the mantle, and asked the Reverend to follow him. They would view the remains of his friend. The actor led the way to a dark chamber where a bed stood in one corner. As best the Reverend could tell, the room was otherwise empty, until Mr. Booth shone the light into the opposite corner, and there lay an irregular heap of objects on a sheet. It took Rev. Clarke a few moments to make sense of what he was seeing: a bushel or more of dead wild pigeons. Kneeling beside them, Mr. Booth held one bird at a time to his heart, murmuring endearments and stroking its feathers.

The astonished minister at first thought the actor was playing an elaborate joke on him. Mr. Booth's earlier recitations, however, and the tears running down his cheeks, convinced him that Mr. Booth was entirely serious.

"He had developed a madman's obsession toward animals and the sacredness of all life."

These were Rev. Clarke's very words as he finished his story. It was then that I began to sympathize with Mr. Booth and question the Reverend's compassion, which seemed in short supply.

An immense course of pigeons had flown over Louisville that week, and the large number slaughtered and sold on street corners was the apparent cause of Mr. Booth's great distress. He had bought up as many of the dead as he could.

"Any sane man," the Reverend commented, "would have realized that the slaughter was negligible. It wouldn't have made a dent in Earth's staggering numbers of pigeons."

Mr. Booth, however, viewed the massacre as a wasteful and barbarous murder scene.

He wanted to publicly testify against this massacre. He wanted to pay a carpenter to make a coffin for the birds, to hire a hearse and carriage, and to hold a formal funeral in a one of the city's respectable burial grounds. He asked if Rev. Clarke might assist him with these tasks, but the Reverend refused. The Reverend had been ready to help with arrangements for a human, but he could not sanction a formal burial for a bushel of birds.

Midnight had come and gone, and Mother was nodding off in her chair.

At last Reverend Clarke wrapped up his account.

Without his help, Mr. Booth had managed to arrange a procession for his birds and a proper burial in a cemetery. According to the Reverend, other signs of the actor's insanity spilled out for as long as the troupe was in town. He sat weeping beside the grave during the day, and at the theater he grieved backstage. He fed apples to delivery horses, imploring their drivers to treat them kindly. He purchased meat for stray dogs and fish for cats, and crouched in alleyways talking to both.

Concluded the Reverend, "The poor man is clearly insane, although his insanity is rather endearing, tied as it is to a warm, not a cold, heart."

The Reverend seemed the heartless one, and I was not sorry when he at last took his umbrella and departed into the night.

February 28, 1840

An outbreak of smallpox in Salem has thankfully been contained, two lives lost.

Sad news from our town is that both husband and wife Townsend have succumbed to lung fever, and elderly Mrs. Wheeler no longer knows her children. One daughter cares for her, and your angel of a mother visits her old friend almost every day.

Father believes you are somewhere below the Australian continent, prowling those seas for tangible evidence of the world's southernmost continent. I wish you could take your pocket watch, face it to a star above and reflect a ray of light back to your Boston family, a sign you are safe & well.

With warm affection, your Cath

To Charles Pickering aboard the USS Vincennes
From Catharine Pickering, Boston

March 15, 1840

My Dear Pickle,

James and I attended a memorable concert tonight at the Odeon. Thunderous applause for the piano-forte of a gentleman from Germany, Louis Rackemann, lasted five minutes.[86] He's said to be the best pianist to step foot in this country—which doesn't seem an exaggeration. My head is on fire with the notes of Liszt, Beethoven, Thalberg, and the young romantic, Chopin. The piano, the daguerreotype—the innovations arriving from Europe are so impressive, everyone wonders what's next?

You'd think after so much rhapsodic music I'd easily fall asleep, but my eyes refuse to close. So stay awake with me & I will relate more goings-on at L'Histoire.

Our curators can talk of nothing else—there's been another Mastodon finding on New York soil![87] It's as if a great energy force is bringing their big bones to the surface, so many are coming to light. Still none found in New England, however. Dr. Binney thinks it's because these animals were not saltwater enthusiasts, preferring alluvial grounds away from the ocean's cold shoulder. New York has yielded several, but the skull has shattered each time oxen have tried to pull it from the ground. Thus the excitement over a skull successfully extricated near the Canadian border, the first example of a fully preserved head without a defect. It's as if the animal died yesterday, the Courier reports.[88] The excavators have suspended it from the beams of a barn and the jaws work together like "a large, magnificent grinding machine."

I assumed Mastodons were carnivorous. Wouldn't an animal so massive require meat in its diet? Yet the historian Mr. Mayborne gave evidence to the contrary at a recent lecture. His knowledge of the ancient lands that comprise New York is all-encompassing.

"The territory of New York was like Africa in those ancient days, teeming with wild animals!" began Mr. Mayborne, a broad-shouldered man with thick gray hair and shaggy eyebrows. "The forests were crowded with bear, fox and wolf, moose and deer, as well as Mammoth, an animal heavier than an elephant. There was an abundance of food; and few armed men molested the wild quadrupeds. Given this prosperous setting, they thrived and often were larger than their European counterparts. Bears, it's said, routinely reached

400 lbs. Today, we fear bears, but back then they seldom posed a threat. They preferred the taste of grasses and berries to the boney, sinewy meat of other creatures. Large moose were also extremely plentiful. Come winter, herds of fifteen or twenty headed deep into the forest, to shelters that the Indians called "moose-yards," where they fed off moss and saplings.

"The Indians, as well as the Europeans after they arrived, had an easy time killing moose; they put up no resistance. One explorer recounted that he and an old brave were paddling across a river, when they came alongside a calf swimming to the other side and stroked its ears. The wide-eyed animal looked up in our faces with the fearless innocence of a house lamb, while making use of its fore foot almost every instant to bat mosquitoes from its eyes."

Mr. Mayborne paused to blow his nose. It suddenly occurred to me that he himself looked like a big, shaggy Mastodon!

"When the settlers arrived and saw this throng of animals, they thought *food*! They also thought *danger*! To cancel out their fear, they had their weapons. But their weapons cancelled out any chance of loving the animals they shared the forest with. As Chief Metacom observed, *You can't keep love and a gun in the same pouch*."[89]

Some of the area's original quadrupeds, like the Mammoth and the black moose, had gone extinct long before the Europeans crossed. After their arrival, because of their chopping down of trees and liberal use of guns, many other animals instinctively fled north.

"The Mastodon!" Mr. Mayborne shrugged his great shoulders. "I became intrigued by the question, what became of this grand creature? My initial hunch was that it was a carnivore that had run out of food. For clues, each time a well-preserved Mastodon came to light, I travelled to the site to examine the contents of its stomach.

"And stomachs don't lie. Inside each one I found a mixture of leaves, aquatic plants, grasses, and broken twigs. Sometimes four to six bushels' worth! I'm convinced, therefore, that this beast was a vegetation feeder and disagree with those who say it ate animals, even small animals. None of my critics have peered into a Mastodon belly, and yet they dole out their opinions!"

He then passed around two impressive molars, one measuring ten inches across and both as heavy as bricks.

"The creature's teeth—more proof! Look at the conical protrusions on the surface! Note the absence of serrated edges found on the teeth of flesh-eaters.

These teeth, ladies and gentlemen, were for grinding vegetable substances, not for carving squirrel! No, the Mastodon didn't lack for food; its dinner grew everywhere! In my less-than-humble opinion, some planetary disaster toppled this beast, not dietary impoverishment."

If the Mastodon wasn't a meat eater, I must side all the more with Mr. Booth. Why do smaller and meeker animals like humans require meat?

James has an interesting theory—that guns have turned us into carnivores! The more weapons manufactured, the more animals shot, the more meat went to market! It's easier to shoot an animal for food, he points out, than to struggle growing crops.

Or, said another way, perhaps we've become carnivorous because we are lazy!

March 26, 1840

Dr. Binney refers to last week as "The Week of the Eggs," because of some unusual occurrences at our Boston Society. First, a dealer from Yonkers stopped by and tried to peddle a large greenish, blackish egg as a dragon's egg. Dr. Binney was patient with the man, at least initially.

—And how did you come by this egg?

—It was brought to this shore by a sailor acquaintance from Siberia.

—And where did the sailor stumble on such a treasure?

—A Siberian friend of his found it in a cave in the mountains.

—And did this friend of a friend steal it from under the dragon?

—No, but the dragon was nearby.

—And how did this friend of a friend know the dragon was nearby?

—He said that when he approached the cave, he heard heavy breathing coming from inside and hid in the bushes. When he spied the dragon leaving, he entered the cave and found two eggs, but carried only one away with him.

— A nice story. But there's no proof this is a dragon's egg, is there? So there's only one thing to do. Before the dealer could protest, Dr. Binney rapped the egg sharply on the rim of the water basin, the contents spilling out and revealing an embryo with developing wings. An emu, it turns out.

I asked Dr. Binney how he so quickly identified the bird.

"The shell! As well as the absence of a dragon's tail," he said with a grin.

If the dealer has any sense, he won't try such conniving again. Museum collectors are becoming wise to con artists.

The second egg to land in our midst does have believable origins. It's a Great Auk egg, large and speckled and beautifully symmetrical. It belonged to the Vicomte de Barde for thirty-odd years, and then, in 1825, traveled to the Boulogne Museum with the rest of his collection. An Englishman acquired it through the exchange of an Ostrich skin and later placed it in an auction in London. It was snatched up by a curator from New Zealand, who eventually put it in another auction, which returned it to London, and it's there that Lucy Pratt pounced on it, purchasing it for ten times its original price.

So, thanks to Lucy, it's now on permanent display in our Museum. Has any egg traveled so widely? Lucy's one caveat is that it can never be sold. The Auks are becoming rare, and in all likelihood, they will be gone someday, and the value of their eggs will soar. But, she stresses, like everything in Nature, an egg has no value, it's priceless.

We think of you often, and miss you every hour,
Cath

SPRING, 1895

Yes, Sophie, for a period of time Mastodon discoveries were constantly in the news. It had a lot to do with Mastodons and Mammoths having been identified as extinct species a few decades before.[90] Now when farmhands digging up marl hit hard porous material, and saw the size of the bone, they had a good idea of what they had struck, whereas their grandfathers hadn't a clue and simply dug around the obstacle.

(In Mexico, when Mammoth bones were discovered in the Valley of Teotihuacan, they were thought to be the remains of giants, giants who had built the pyramids there.)

The first mastodon skeleton found in the United States turned up in a marl pit near Newburgh, New York, in 1799. It was sold to Charles Willson Peale, who had gone from being one of America's most respected portrait artists to starting a natural history museum in Philadelphia. The enormous skeleton became "the ninth wonder of the world" and helped make Peale's museum famous. The fossil was mistakenly ascribed to a "mammoth"—the mastodon not identified as a separate species until a few years later—and confusion between the two lasted for several years. Small world that it was, Charles Peale's youngest son, Titian, was one of the naturalists sailing on the U.S. Exploring Expedition and worked closely with Charles collecting bird and mammal specimens as well as ethnographic objects.

Here's a strange coincidence! In 1844, a farmer would stumble upon five mastodon skeletons in the vicinity of Hackettstown, New Jersey. Who caught wind of the discovery, but Dr. Webster, the chemistry professor who later murdered Dr. Parkman![91] Webster deluded himself the way Capt. Eades had when he paid a small fortune for the Feejee Mermaid. If he purchased one of these fantastic fossils, he thought the income from exhibiting it to the public would allow him to repay Dr. Parkman and others to whom he owed money. He borrowed $3000 from several prominent citizens to make the purchase. But for some reason, the fossil was never displayed, and Webster fell deeper into desperate straits. Which led to his borrowing money from Dr. Parkman in 1849, and then killing him because he couldn't pay it back. Good god!

Don't you wish Earth still had those great creatures? And Great Auks too?! If those large stubby-winged birds still existed, we'd be able to canoe out to the islands of Boston Bay, where they once thrived, and picnic among them.

The slaughter of all seabirds increased dramatically in the eighteenth century, in parallel with the growing presence of guns. Not that guns were necessary for obtaining Great Auks. Their capture was as easy as chasing them up planks from the beach onto a boat. By 1844, only two were left in the world, residents of a rookery off Iceland. Three Icelandic fishermen landed on the rock in June of that year. They found one egg, only one, and it was broken.

When they carried off the last two individuals, they virtually extinguished the species' chance for recovery and a future.

To Charles Pickering aboard the USS Vincennes
From Catharine Pickering, Boston

April 11, 1840

Dearest Charles,

The *Courier* informs us that the *Sea Gull* hasn't been seen since leaving Terra del Fuego with the rest of the Fleet in June, and that the small schooner may have gone down in a gale. For all we know you might have changed ships, and uncertainty would be gnawing away at us were it not for your letter from Callao. Thank heavens for that letter! —even though your vivid descriptions don't exactly ease our minds. The sea sounds like an occasional monster. And your ship, a pathetic twig.

As for the *Relief* being smoked to rid it of rats—good grief, what a hellhole. We sincerely hope the cats on the *Vincennes* are doing their job!

Here, the transition from winter to spring is as pokey as ever. My three charges have premature spring fever, and to calm their wiggles I took them to our society's Museum yesterday. The visit worked wonders. I've never seen them so absorbed. The giant ground sloth in the vestibule awoke quite a discussion, as did the stuffed ant bear in the main hall.

"It doesn't look like an ant!" said Abigail with usual outspokenness.

It's a mammal that eats ants and termites, I offered.

"It eats ants and it's so big?!" Peals of laughter from Ollie.

"They run up its nose?" asked Sarah.

Shrieks of merriment from all three.

"I ate an ant once by mistake and it didn't taste good!" shared Sarah.

When we came to the room that holds Mr. Couthouy's shell collection, Ollie pressed his nose to the case, trying to see inside the coiled recesses of a Syrinx aruanus.

"What lives inside?" he asked.

No one is exactly sure, I said. In fact, Capt. Couthouy and Cousin Charles were in the South Seas investigating that very question.[92] The interior dweller might actually make its shell.

"Like Matilda?" Sarah asked. Yes, sort of like Matilda, who was her turtle.

They spent a long time examining the basket starfish and its lacey arms.

"That's an animal?" Sarah asked, wide-eyed. "It's pretty."

"It's pretty because God made it!" pronounced Abigail, again with startling conviction.

Nature shaped and formed it over a long period of time, I offered, when I probably should have left them to their own imaginings.

A few days later I received a note from Abigail's mother written in broad swirls: "Whatever did you mean when you told Abigail that nature, not God, was responsible for making the marine creature she described as a lovely lace doily? You were wrong to put such ideas in her head. I'm afraid I have no choice but to withdraw my daughter from your classes. —Constance Warburton"

I will sorely miss Abigail, and only hope her curiosity never fades. On the way out of the Museum, she pointed to the whale suspended from the ceiling, specifically one part, and asked what it was, and I told her. Possibly she repeated my response to her mother and that was the real reason for my dismissal. I simply said it was for making little whales. Oh, the dangers inherent in a whale!

April 16, 1840

The staff at the Society is in a state of shock, good shock that is, due to Col. Perkin's gift of Mr. Audubon's *Birds of America*. The four volumes are bound in Russian leather, and the set is said to be the most valuable in the country.

With his series of *Bird* plates completed and behind him, Audubon is now working on a similar series of quadrupeds. If he conveys his animals with the respect he does his birds, we will again be in his debt.

No, you are not mistaken. My feelings for Mr. Audubon are gradually warming. Col. Perkins swears that the artist has a tender side, a disposition that agonizes over man's cruelties to animals, and that every day he grows more exasperated with the scoundrels who wage war on birds entirely for the marketplace and profit.[93] The Colonel accompanied Mr. Audubon on a trip to Labrador some years back where they witnessed the murderous eggers, the masses of marine birds they killed or left dying, the newborns and chicks they trampled, as well as their pillage of every egg to be found.[94]

Col. Perkins sums it up this way. Eggers work for the Devil. Who else but the Devil's henchmen can look at something so beautiful as an egg and remove it from its mother and her nest? The Colonel swears that the awful sights on that northern rock were a turning point for Mr. Audubon, and that the artist's trigger-happy days are over.

Shouldn't the exquisiteness of a painted bird make people less inclined to kill them? That thought alone makes me think better of the artist.

April 19, 1840

Mr. Draper of New York has created a remarkable daguerreotype of the moon. Several papers published the image. Mr. Daguerre made a similar picture last year, but Mr. Draper's image is far sharper and captures the mysterious dark plains scattered across the moon's surface. He also uses a gas microscope to make pictures of minutiae. A fly's wing, a drop of blood, a parade of animalcules! As Father observes, our new inventions are pushing us into the realm of the invisible, a place beyond our comprehension.

I feel that way about James Cutting, in a place I've never been before. It's easier saying this to you in a letter, because if you were here, my curious cousin would be after details, and I wouldn't have many to offer. Other than, James Cutting makes me laugh, like you do!

Father notices. He winked at me yesterday when I went out wearing a new scarf.

April 26, 1840

Less rain fell in Boston last year than in many previous years. The Courier reports that Boston saw only 34.82 inches in 1839, whereas in 1831, 50.87 inches were measured.[95] No wonder Salem had such a poor corn crop last summer. This month we are headed toward spring quite waterlogged.

Other news. Your friend Seth Lawrence has established a new business on Prince Street. He's supplying physicians with leeches from France. They are imported in clay in wooden boxes and advertised as the world's "best." Father wonders how you can tell a good leech from a bad leech, and thinks Seth would be wiser, from a cost standpoint, to simply get his leeches from nearby ponds. Seth, meanwhile, is attempting to breed the French variety, lured by a $500 subsidy from the government.[96]

I showed Oliver the fleet's progress on a globe, and he asked me again, what did people on the other side of the world look like? Do they have horse bodies? Do they have long noses? Were they ten feet tall like the giraffe man? He's possibly picked up these notions from fanciful exhibits at the Boston Museum. I assured him they look like the rest of us with very few differences.

Once you arrive home, be prepared for a flood of questions!

With love, Cath

To Charles Pickering aboard the USS Vincennes
From Catharine Pickering, Boston

May 2, 1840

Dear Cousin,

Forgive me for starting with bad news, but last month slid in that direction. Our cousin Sally's pregnancy terminated early with a still-born boy. Her sisters are assisting with household chores while gently reminding her that she has five other children who need her care and attention. But she remains vacant and depressed. Also, your school friend Sam Forbes received a terrible injury. A tree felling went wrong, and his leg was crushed so badly, it had to be amputated. He's seen a specialist in Connecticut and will be fitted with a new style of cork prosthesis. He's always been a cheerful soul, and his bad luck hasn't crushed that part of him.

Father swears that someday we'll have a device for recording sound, just as the camera records sights. Had I such a device, I would have canned last Wednesday's lecture for you. Mr. Branch, a zoologist from Philadelphia, spoke on a subject you bring up all the time—animal intelligence and how creatures are brighter and more capable of memory and emotions than people realize. The dog that does math. The horse that picks locks. He told a lovely account about all the fish that gather whenever a farmer plays his flute beside a pond. But his most interesting examples came from the deeper wild—animals doing whatever they need to do to survive.

"The clever wolverine climbs a tree carrying a clump of moss in his mouth, a very special moss that deer find tasty," related Mr. Branch, "and once comfortably stretched out on a limb, he drops the moss on the ground below and patiently waits. Along comes an unsuspecting deer who starts eating the moss. Down leaps the wolverine from his hiding place, rips open the deer and has his own tasty meal."[97]

Someone in the audience asked whether brain size corresponded with intelligence.

"*No, no, no!*" asserted Mr. Branch, a small excitable man with a mustache the width of his head. "Insects can be plenty smart, despite a pinprick of a brain."

"A couple who travel the world studying wasps saw this astonishing sight. Digger-wasps in the West picking up small pebbles with their mandibles and using them like hammers, to loosen pieces of dirt they then used for nest-making. *Yes, yes, yes!*

"As for common brown wasps, they may have passed some of their ingenuity on to humans! You've seen the paper nests they make—they resemble hanging lanterns. They chew wood from rotted stumps, moisten it with a secretion, and spit out wood pulp. It's suspected that we learned the art of paper-making by watching them. *Yes, yes, yes!*

"In reverse, wasps have borrowed from humans! They collect bits and pieces of the paper bags we put over grape plants and spit them out for making their nests. Which saves them from making their own paper. So clever, *yes, yes, yes!*"

May 21, 1840

The Public Garden's tulip beds have opened for the season. James and I walked around the entire perimeter. The new plantings took our breath away, with many prizewinners from Europe among the thousands in bloom. But poor Mr. Teschemacher is once more apoplectic. Someone stole into the beds one night and made off with at least two dozen flowers, and, when we encountered him, his face was the color of the tulip that won the Queen of England's top prize, a deep vermillion. Poor man, he tries so.

We also stopped at Dr. Gray's Conservatory to view the large plants with multiple red flowers that Capt. Poinsett brought back from Mexico. Dr. Gray plans to add them to the outer beds, these plants everyone is calling "Poinsettias."

The Conservatory has many more exotic birds than when I last visited, including curassows from a menagerie in Holland. One of the directors has left for Brazil to bring back still others & attempt their domestication.

May 27, 1840

An early morning fire in a building around the corner from Father's office cloaked the downtown in ash yesterday. The cause was a familiar one—a gas light was left burning in an unoccupied room, and when the building's other lamps were extinguished, the pressure in this remaining lamp pushed the flame so high, the ceiling caught fire. Fire crews got there quickly, and the building, although badly scorched, was saved.

Father is convinced that Boston is such a tinderbox, a large fire will consume it unless new methods of illumination, notably electricity, replace lighting by explosive, gassy means. Fire, he points out, can travel much faster than horse-pulled equipment![98] "Boston is tempting fate!"

The *Flying Gypsy* is about to sail for the Sandwiches, where your Squadron will return eventually, so I'll run our packet down to the docks before it leaves.[99] We have you somewhere in the western Pacific—possibly between Australia and the Feejees. I hope by now that you've laid eyes on the large Hawaiian goose so loved by your deceased friend Mr. Douglas; also, that you have drunk strong island rum from a coconut.

Always with love, Cath

SPRING, 1895

Sophie Bear, back in 1840, Boston was still a small city in a still small world. How small a world? The amateur botanist credited with introducing a brilliant red flower from Mexico to this country, the famous "Christmas" plant that Mr. Teschemacher brought to the Public Garden, and the government official who chose Charles Wilkes to lead the Exploring Expedition, were one and the same: Joel Poinsett, the country's Secretary of War. Small enough, too, that Uncle John Pickering and Col. Poinsett were old friends.

A decade earlier, while serving as the country's first minister to Mexico, Col. Poinsett was so dazzled by a crimson flower with "painted leaves" that he sent cuttings back to his greenhouse in South Carolina. Gardens throughout Europe and America were abloom with the festive "poinsettia" by 1840.

Color! It was a subtle development, but Boston and other American cities were gradually awakening to the vibrant hues that were sweeping in from foreign ports in the form of flowers, painted porcelains, searing dyes and pigments. Bright colors so often were the product of places where the sun shone hotly. Even Daguerre's photographs evoked color, the color that was originally missing in those images and soon applied by tinting.

The artists of the U.S. Exploring Expedition were keenly aware of the hours they might have saved had they been able to photograph the subtle pastels of the living animal inside a seashell, the translucent hues of fish scales, or the waning colors of a dying bird's plumage. Delicate colors were so difficult to replicate by hand. As it was, the artists had so many specimens to draw, they frequently turned work over to the Scientifics, or provided only enough of a drawing to guide colorists back in Washington who filled in the rest.

To Charles Pickering aboard the USS Vincennes
From Catharine Pickering, Boston

June 10, 1840

Dearest Charles,

A sailor off the *Neptune* delivered your absorbing letter sent from Sydney, which reassures us you are safe and well. Or at least you were last November. Oh, the frustrating delay between letters! What a complete sense you give of the Aborigines, as well as the natives you met sailing from atoll to atoll on your Pacific crossing. Your close call on one Coral isle filled us with dread.[100] As much as I loathe guns, I'm glad you are sometimes armed when you set foot on those remote beaches.

I write from Salem, where Mother, Mary and I will be spending the summer. Mother has a persistent cough, and her doctor feels that country air is the best medicine. I ride the rail into town twice a week, for various tasks at L'Histoire and for tutoring. Father rides out to Salem on weekends. We think that, as the railroads expand, Boston families will increasingly pack their summer trunks and disappear into the country. More and more friends are doing this. Also due to the rails, formerly remote areas are attracting a wave of new businesses.[101]

On Sunday we supped with our neighbor Mr. Hathorne. He had shot a moose in Broad Field and asked us to share its culinary effects. I found the meal less than appetizing, for along with flank steaks, on the platter were parts of the animal not commonly served—the nose, which Mr. Hathorne calls "an epicurean delight," and the tongue. Both were mild-tasting and tender, although I consumed little of either.

Father sent me a look that said, *Dear girl, eat what's on your plate!* My look back said, *I simply can't!* I'm aware that my habits are changing—devouring the leg of such a superb creature makes me cringe, when once it didn't. And doesn't grilled meat lying beside the pretty greens of asparagus and sprouts on Wedgwood fool us into forgetting how recently that poor animal was happy in the wood?

Every day I drift closer to Mr. Booth in attitude. If someday I'm also seen as having lost my senses, I'll consider it a great compliment.

June 12, 1840

So much in your last letter intrigues us, particularly the way the natives of Tahiti get everything they need from Nature & want for nothing. I'm envious of such an existence. Here in New England, we think of ourselves as thrifty. Yet our possessions constantly multiply. The more we have, the more we desire. The more we desire, the more merchants import, the more the newspapers advertise them, the more we purchase.

Calcutta silk, Egyptian cashmere, London hats, Holland gin and Turkish tobacco. Offerings by manufacturers on our own shore are reaching new levels of absurdity. The Atlas advertises a new "Oxygen Soap" that removes "freckles, pimples, sunburn and deposits of bile on the skin."[102] I'd be afraid it would remove my nose!

James and I went to feed the swans on Mr. Hathorne's pond last Sunday and observed the most amazing sight. Another Troc'ulus for you! Instead of snatching up the bread, one of the swans pushed a piece just beyond him, and after a patient spell of pushing & waiting, pushing & waiting, a small fish swam to the surface to take the bread, and low-and-behold the swan took the fish and bread in one gulp. We threw out more pieces of bread, and the bird kept this cleverness up, catching two more fish. James named the inventive swan—Leonardo Defishie!

At supper—James had returned to Boston—Mother kept staring at me, I guess because, after recounting the incident, I kept laughing and found it hard to keep a straight face. Father always knows precisely what's going on in my head. When I passed him the onions, he gave me one of his winks.

Be well and safe, your loving cousin

SPRING, 1895

Sophie, the letter Cath refers to has been lost. But the following might interest you—Charles' journal account of the crew's attempts to land on the Pacific island of Tepoto in August 1839.[103] One can't blame the natives for distrusting them, given earlier instances of armed and aggressive foreigners clamoring onto their island.

> Three boats left the ship, and we found 18 Natives, men & boys, collected to oppose our landing, half a dozen of them armed with long, pointed lances of Cocoa-nut wood, but we saw no other weapons. The surf was so gentle that we could almost take the boats near enough to leap on the coral. The Natives were continually calling to us and motioning us to be off and pointing their lances towards us, although they seemed very glad to get the presents we threw on shore and wanted more.[104]
>
> Capt. Wilkes having given our boat permission to attempt landing, we separated from the others and approached the shore, and three of our party leaped into the water. A midshipman first reached the shore & almost immediately a man came running down from the other party, who appeared to be the Chief, with a lance, and the lad was forced to retreat. All three then returned to the boat. The Natives began to throw stones, especially the boys. As far as we could make out, they did not want war but wanted us away from the shore. Finding it impossible to do anything with them and time growing short, we administered a little mustard seed to their legs, evidently with some effect—one of them was observed endeavoring to wash it off. He, the Chief, and the rest removed to the wood, and we went back to our ship.

Charles tells of another encounter a month later, a much more peaceful one with the inhabitants of Tahiti. He realized he was glimpsing technologies at primitive stages, and this fascinated him.[105]

I rose at 5 a.m. and was informed that our guide was already fishing! We were camped in a small valley between high peaks, which had but a slight stream tickling by, and we were surprised to learn that in the water there were eels. There was a slight basin at the foot of the cliff, where an eel was concealed, and the Native placed a large flat stone in the middle of this basin and commenced bailing out the water with his hands. He disturbed the fish which, as anticipated, took refuge under this stone; he then cautiously inserted his hand and grasping the eel threw it 30 or 40 feet into the woods, & gave chase. In this manner two were taken, one of them nearly four feet in length. The eels, later served for breakfast, were carefully cleaned and then cut in pieces, which were wrapped in leaves and cooked in the usual manner. Later, desirous of procuring some small fish we saw in the stream, our guide set to work again. He formed a small noose from the Poorow bark, and fixing it at the end of a little twig went into the water. It was not long before he had one of them swinging round over his head and brought it to shore.

These people are the least helpless of any I have read of. Strip an Indian entirely in the morning and without an implement in his hand, turn him into the woods; then pay him a visit at night. We shall find him clothed from the lace of the Cocoa-nut tree, a garland on his head; a house over him, made of the Wild Bananas; thongs & cordage of all sorts from the bark of the Poorow tree; baskets made by plaiting the segments of a Cocoa-nut leaf; perhaps a mat to sleep on; cups or wash-bowls of Cocoa-nut shell, or even tumblers & casks of the joints of the large Bamboo; a Cap or an Umbrella if it is wanted of the Banana leaf; a fire kindled; all the appurtenances of the culinary art…enough for a week.

To Charles Pickering aboard the USS Vincennes
From Catharine Pickering, Boston

July 9, 1840
Dearest Cousin,
    We woke up to the headline "Highly Important Discovery" this morning,

and celebrated with creamed eggs & cognac! Each of us tried to recall what we were doing on January 19th, when so far away the *Vincennes* was proving beyond a shadow of a doubt the existence of the great Antarctic Continent?[106] I was dusting the bird egg cabinet—while you were making history!

The Boston Courier's account was heart-stopping. How close the *Vincennes* came to drifting into the ice pack. The severity of the cold! Even your beaver coat must have felt thin and inadequate. Yet the satisfaction of beholding that coastline, and only a few days before the French appeared on the horizon. And capturing the Antarctic's prominent headlands with the camera lucida! Dr. Binney is already talking about holding a large celebration and displaying those images once you're home.

Here, it's practically the opposite—warm and wet. One of the rainiest summers in memory. Most everyone's carriage has gotten stuck, and even the Providence rail was halted by water flooding the tracks.

Quite miraculously, the sun shone on June 24th for Boston's celebration of the 400th anniversary of the invention of printing. Shops were closed; buildings were robed in flags and banners. A long procession of printers, booksellers, authors and readers wrapped through the downtown streets. You would have known many of the faces. Both our Salem neighbor, Mr. Hathorne, and Salem's favorite author Mr. Hawthorne—whose *Twice Told Tales* is selling briskly, I might add—were present. A festive seafood dinner at Faneuil Hall ran long because of the talks and toasts.

It was easy to feel proud of our city, given all the pomp, truth and humor that lasted nearly all day long. The Mayor's toast raised a loud roar of approval: "Long live the art of printing! Let's hope it eventually improves men's minds as much as it lengthens their tongues."

A telegram sent by the distinguished printer Benjamin True got a loud cheer:

"Gentlemen, I was gratified to receive an invitation to your celebration, but I am too old a type, and could not make the journey. I have been in use for seventy-five years, and expect soon to be put into the old shoe—there to remain till the great type founder above shall see fit to cast me over."[107]

July 16, 1840

One cabinet that people always huddle around at the Society is its collection of bird nests. It continues to grow, thanks to Henry Thoreau. He brought in more of the hanging variety yesterday—the grassy loop of the marsh wren, the strong pouch of the golden robin. Human hands can hardly match the fineness of their weave.

He glanced down at the morning paper I was reading and grimaced. I thought he'd seen the headline about a barge overturning, ten drowned. But no. He grimaced because he dislikes newspapers and thinks they're a waste of time.

"You call that news? Nothing's new in this world! Nothing. Drama and death, death and drama over and over, repurposed with different names, different places. If you've read about a man poisoned, a dog shot, chickens eaten, crops ravaged or a house struck by lightning, what more do you need to know? If you grasp the basic notion that bad things happen, more examples don't seem terribly necessary and just dampen the day."

Mr. Chase has taken to calling Henry "Hank the Crank." He does have a critical nature, and always an axe to grind. But his points are well taken.

SPRING, 1895

Sophie, never say never. This is certainly an instance of why.

Captain Cook, after failing to find the Great Southern Continent in the 1770s, decided those icy polar seas were too risky for further exploration. "I can be bold enough to say that no man will ever venture farther than I have done; and that the lands which may lie to the south will never be explored," he predicted.[108] But men did; and lands were.

Imagine your cousin Charles—gripping the railing of the *Vincennes*, the frosty air turning his nose and ears bright red, the wind practically lifting him off his feet—taking part in that enormous discovery. After recording a distinct view of a headland on January 19, 1840, the Wilkes fleet continued to skirt the coastline of Antarctica for more than fifteen-hundred nautical miles, a territory that Cook emphatically stated was too treacherous to reach, even if it did exist.

To Charles Pickering aboard the USS Vincennes
From Catharine Pickering, Boston

September 3, 1840

Dear Cousin,

Last week, one of the worst hurricanes in memory pretty much unhinged everyday life. In its aftermath, the newspapers are filled with questions. What causes such strong winds? Can we predict their arrival with greater precision? Mr. Spooner, a Natural History member, thinks a force inside Earth causes them, since sometimes they coincide with earthquakes.[109]

James has a different theory having to do with ocean temperature and air pressure, which I don't pretend to understand.

"In the 12th Century, people thought thunder occurs when frozen clouds collide and come tumbling down," he commented. "So will Mr. Spooner's theory. Kaplunkaphooey!"

Increasingly the bird population has my heartfelt concern. Hardly a day goes by without my hearing another unhappy tale. Yesterday, an English visitor to our Museum related an incident that still haunts him. He and a friend were hunting near Ambleside, when they spied a chaffinch sitting on a bough and spotted its nest in an ivy-clad tree fifty feet away. He shot the bird—a female, it turned out. The next week, returning to the same forest, he was curious to see if the chaffinch's nest held eggs. So he climbed the large tree and made a heartbreaking discovery. A male chaffinch lay dead in the nest, not a mark on him, and under his outstretched wings were four lifeless baby birds. When its mate hadn't returned, the male either pined to death or couldn't bear to leave the young ones and starved to death.[110]

The hunter gave the male chaffinch to London's Natural History Museum. Its small stiff body maintains its protective position, and everyone who sees it is deeply moved. The Englishman was so altered by the event, his desire to shoot birds completely dried up.

"And now I have to wonder why I ever hunted birds in the first place! If birds could talk like humans, would we take their lives? There's something to think about!"

Sept. 18, 1840

Your fascinating letter from Feejee—I've read it over at least five times. You said I'd think you "strange" because of your reaction to the island's natives. Far from it. Everything you describe is so alien to our own culture, no wonder you came away bewildered.

Last night James and I attended a reception for Lord Pembroke of London, and now it's my turn to say that I'm bewildered by *our* natives. We never laid eyes on Lord Pembroke, but someone hard to miss was Boston's doyenne of fashion, Louisa Sparks. If her new fall bonnet of a blinding saffron is any indication, French fashions are approaching the grotesque. Its brim was trimmed with curled ostrich and marabout feathers. The most "*distingué* of plumes, Lydia Macomber would have you believe. I would add, if they are on the bird, not off. Lydia's bonnet was also a raft of feathers, although slightly fewer that Louisa's.

James whispered in my ear—"ruddiculosis!"

The feather imports have been depressed for some time. But now they are on the rise, and the general consensus is that fashion hounds will increasingly embrace hats with feathers. All kinds of feathers. I worry that soon there will be more feathers walking around Boston than flying in the air. (I may be forced to buy a shotgun.) When I shared my dislike of this trend with Father, he told me I must try to be more tolerant of "human exigencies."

"But Catharine"—this is how he always begins whenever he's trying to sway me away from some idea. "But Catharine, the history of human fashion is festooned with feathers." He gave the example of Marie Antoinette, whose own brother called "featherhead." The headdresses she and her friends wore rose so high in the air, it made it seem their heads were positioned in the middle of their bodies! Father did an imitation, walking around our living room with a high stack of books on his head.

Mother and I had a good laugh. Mother, God bless her, declared that no feathers will ever sit atop her head, and I gave her a big kiss for that.

James and I attended a performance by Fanny Elssler at the Tremont. The theater hasn't seen such large audiences since the days of *La Sonnambula*. The tickets were expensive but it was worth every penny to watch this extraordinary Austrian dancer execute her famous "Cachucca," which she is dancing straight across the country. The garlands and wreaths thrown onstage could have filled our Beacon Street parlor.

This small fellow hopped about on the windowsill this morning. I know you think house sparrows are crowding out other kinds, and yet like all birds they add levity and possibility to our own gravity-stricken world.

SPRING, 1895

Catharine's illness waxed and waned. Some days, she felt quite strong. Other days, she felt so out-of-sorts and tired, she kept to her room. Its windows overlooked the Public Garden, and, using a small brass scope made by James, she studied various birds and became quite adept at sketching them.

To Charles Pickering aboard the USS Vincennes
From Catharine Pickering, Boston

October 15, 1840

Rumors fly, set loose by sailors on returning ships and the letters they bring back. Is it true that when Capt. Couthouy fell ill during the fleet's stopover in the Samoans, Capt. Wilkes took advantage of the situation to dismiss him from the Expedition? Mary and I received a newsy letter from him some months ago, but he said nothing of irreconcilable differences and instead marveled over the fact that half of the shells your Scientifics were collecting represent new species. But now we hear he's convalescing in the Sandwiches & will return to Boston when he's well enough to travel.

By the way, Ollie is tantalized by the mystery of the shell dwellers & the possibility that they make the spheres they live in. He's full of good questions. This particular one he's asked twice:

- -How can a soft body make a hard shell?

Knowing your interest in African animals, I'm passing on this dispatch from the Courier. I'm really not sure what to make of it.

A South African zoologist claims that a creature of fables, the unicorn, could very well be a real animal, a species of Rhinoceros. The "Ndzoo-dzoo"—however that's pronounced—is about the size of a horse and has a single horn protruding from its forehead. When the animal is asleep, its horn is as supple as an elephant's trunk. But once the animal wakes, the horn grows hard and the animal is set to hunt. It has a fierce disposition and chases anything that moves. Its victims often climb up a tree to escape, a fatal mistake, because the Rhinoceros will ferociously butt the tree with his horn, until the tree cracks and splits, and the chased animal topples out and is gored. The corpse is never devoured but left on the ground like a discarded trophy.[111]

I think we should keep on believing in the spotless white animal of myth, don't you?

Sending fond wishes, your devoted cousin

SUMMER, 1895

Sophie, my bear, here's a coincidence. While Catharine's description of the single-horned rhinoceros was making its way to Charles, his letter describing Hawaii's wild cattle and their deadly horns was on its way to Catharine. "Bullocks" brought to Hawaii by an Englishman in the late 18th century had multiplied so furiously, that by the 1830s they were devouring not only the island's crops but natives' thatched roofs. Hawaiians hired professional hunters from overseas to capture the destructive animals in earthen pits dug near the bullocks' watering holes. Someone Charles greatly admired, the Scottish naturalist David Douglas, had fallen into one of these entrapments years earlier and been fatally mauled by a bullock trapped within. The Douglas fir, a tree he discovered, is named after this unfortunate young man.

In his journal, Charles described the pits he came across while climbing the slopes of Mauna Kea. Understandably, his friend's death six years earlier made him study each trap from every angle, hoping to find evidence that David Douglas may not have experienced such a painful finish.

It was drizzling as we made our way up the mountain, and we entered a thick mist. Passing along a narrow gorge with precipitous sides, we came to a small basin of water, the first we had seen today. After filling our water bags, we proceeded along a good clear road, turned off to the right, and found ourselves on the same path that Douglas had followed the morning he lost his life. After a couple of miles, we came to the pits. They are 7 or 8 feet deep, and apparently just large enough to contain a bullock. I would have thought it impossible for a bullock to turn round in one, but am informed they will turn, instantaneously. At first it seemed extremely improbable that Douglas should have met his death in the manner alleged. Some residents believe he was savagely murdered. However, all the testimony I collected during my stay makes me think the published account is correct.

We gathered a few plants as memorials and proceeded. A little further on, our guide showed us a heap of stones, which marks the spot where a Native, attempting to shoot a Bullock like a White Man, was killed by the wounded animal who "carried him on his horn for a couple of hours afterwards," our guide reported. We also heard of a Native, who having finished a pit and nicely tracked it with a bullock's hoof, was so excited when he captured an animal that in his haste, he fell in himself—but being armed with a knife, they were both found dead! It seems bullock-shooting is not without the desired attractions of the chase.

The next day, descending on a muddy path, we came unexpectedly upon a 'Mamani' tree near a deserted hut; and were told that it had been planted by the Bird-catchers to entice the birds. In Honolulu, a variety of small birds are offered for sale. We understand they are also taken by Birdlime made from the Pisonia and its sticky seeds. They call that tree a "catchbird-tree," because of its ensnaring of birds, reptiles and other small creatures. Yes, it's a profession on these islands; and I understand that it is extensively practiced in parts of Europe.[112]

Charles was deeply troubled that David Douglas's remains lay in an unmarked grave. His friends on either side of the Atlantic were erecting monuments to Douglas, but soon no one would be able to point to the actual ground that held his friend's bones.

About Charles' reference to Birdlime, it's a hunting ploy still used in many parts of the world. You wouldn't want to be a bird that lands on a branch covered with this sticky substance. Let's leave it at that.

To Charles Pickering aboard the USS Vincennes
From Catharine Pickering, Boston

December 1, 1840

Dearest Charles,

What a busy correspondent you are!

At Thanksgiving in Salem, most every cousin had something to share about your escapades. We were fourteen adults and a throng of children this year. The dining table was at full extension, its middle piled so high with squashes and fruits, that the smaller fry complained they couldn't see their cousins sitting opposite. James politely made no mention of our odd customs. The boiled turkey with cream sauce at one end of the table. The roasted turkey and stewed cranberries at the other. Uncle Benjamin's masterful job of carving with one arm tied behind him. And the tradition of the youngest walking the table end-to-end. The honor this year went to 16-month-old Gregory, a cute tyke who possesses the weight of Grandfather Timothy's nose, poor thing. He went the distance, though wobbled precariously close to the mince pie.

Ollie was up to his usual monkeyness. After dessert, without anyone noticing, he led several younger cousins over to the henhouse, where an egg fight broke out. If the children's sheepish expressions hadn't given them away, their clothes would have! Great Uncle John marched Oliver off to the coal closet. I found it hard to keep a straight face!

December 5, 1840

My despair over our mistreatment of birds has sunk to a new low. A talk by Mr. Bullington of Philadelphia, who specializes in preserving skins, is why. You would be equally alarmed by his observations. Or lack thereof.

"I frequently travel from Rome to St. Petersburg, Brazil to Africa," he began, "and nowhere is there to be found a single quadruped or bird that has been properly prepared and stuffed according to scientific principles. The lion's face is shrunken; the tiger's ferocity is missing; the bear's fur is matted and lackluster; the fox is bloated; and without fail the legs of birds are dried out and shriveled. A curator at one museum asked my opinion of an enormous skin of an elephant hanging on one wall, and I gave him an honest answer. A better replica could be had by stitching two cow skins together! He didn't like hearing this, but it was true."

Then Mr. Bullington shared his own protocol:

"Immediately treat the skin to make it resist putrefaction and insects. Keep it moist as you go about giving it form and features. Take generously from nature; for many samples are needed to work from. The art of preservation requires patient trial-and-error to bring the animal visually alive. The creator has labored excessively over this animal. So must you!"

Take generously from Nature? Re-engineer the creature as if you're the almighty? I fixed a glare on him that should have eviscerated him on the spot.

"I was recently in Rome," he went on, "to instruct a group of naturalists in preservation. The quantity of birds on sale at Rome's bird-market is nothing short of spectacular. Every day the entire floor of the Rotunda is crowded with venders whose tables are covered with mounds of birds. Hundreds upon hundreds of thrush and blackbird, ringdove, robin red-breast, lark, finch, sparrow and other small flyers. The Romans capture quail with nets from the shores of the Mediterranean, and hundreds of these autumnal travelers are offered by Rome's birdmen as well. The venders might look like rogues, but they are decent Christians within and work hard to earn their way."

Mr. Bullington preserved fifty birds, a badger, and a porcupine while he was in Rome, then set out for Florence to meet with another group.

"Nothing astonished me more than how few birds I saw on my way to Florence. Two noisy blackbirds flying over a marsh, a handful of hooded crows rising off a tree, a few coot, one or two heron. These were the only evidence that winged creatures have not entirely deserted the countryside we travelled through. The quietness was odd and has no explanation. The woods felt eerie without them."

No explanation? When all of Rome and its surrounding towns are feasting on birds of every description? How could Mr. Bullington fail to put two and two together? To use Father's expression, he is a "man without a compass."

Something occurred to me several months ago, but I lacked the courage. Little does he know, but Mr. Bullington has awakened my courage. I've set a meeting date, and an invitation has gone out to several dozen women suggesting we start a salon. It will be devoted to gaining representation at the State House and drafting a few sensible laws to protect our winged friends from undeserved slaughter. Despite the fashion of feathers, women on the whole are more sensitive to guns and their extreme use than men are. We tend to be more gentle foragers. When we walk in the woods, we return with morels and flowers—not a bag of lifeless birds.

Father hasn't been encouraging. He thinks husbands will block the way.

At breakfast, he put down the morning paper, which he almost never does, and looked at me in an unusually serious way. "But Catharine, you must know what you're up against. Most of our Boston and Salem friends hunt—they live for hunting. It invigorates them."

But how is it, I asked, that so many members of the Natural History Society can believe Nature's treasures to be the work of a loving God, and then traipse into the forest to kill that work?

Father looked down at his plate of eggs, bacon strips and chicken livers. "My sweet, don't forget the foodchain."

Father and Mother nevertheless have offered to host the evening. Rev. Peabody will open the meeting with a few remarks about the State's variety of birds, after which I'll talk about our objectives and recruit volunteers. There's little to do but wait & see who appears at our Beacon Street door on the evening of December 14th.

December 17, 1840

Are you guessing the outcome and wincing?

The warning signs began a few days after the invitations went out. Amanda Livingston, whom I ran into at the fish market, said she couldn't attend because of a "pressing engagement." Harriet Warren all but hid from me at Brigham's Provisions. Ruth White sent a note saying her evenings are spent caring for a failing aunt. But it was Lucinda Hovey, when we passed on the street, whose honesty prepared me the most.

"Catharine, a noble cause and I stand by you, I really do. But Arthur isn't keen about my attending. He feels women know too little about birds and their actions to be creating laws to manage them, and it occurs to me that he has a point."

She gave me a regretful look and was gone. I was crestfallen, for Lucinda possesses more commonsense than ten women combined.

When the evening arrived, my stalwarts were there—Mother, Father, Mary, Rev. Peabody and dear James—but only five others in addition, too few for a quorum. I was glum, very glum, but only for a few days. Newspaper reports about gunners robbing our skies persist—and one day the public will snap to. I'm rosier, too, due to an encounter yesterday with Lucinda who was in the park walking her dogs.

"George Putnam boasts of 400 songbirds shot in a day?—it's reprehensible!" She all but shouted this as we came together on the path near the new greenhouse. She, too, had seen the news coverage of Mr. Putnam's repugnant killing spree.

"I've thought it over, and I'd like to lend a hand after all. Arthur has only so much control over me."

Her quick laugh and mischievous glint went a long way toward restoring my own faith in the project—our project now. Lucinda has agreed to be a founding member!

December 24, 1840

There was an unusual accident at the menagerie this week. It's an interesting case and likely to be decided in court. The opinions streaming in make it clear that people are ready to come to the defense of wild creatures, if a situation warrants it.

The man tending the elephant tried to urge the beast to move, and when it didn't budge, he pricked it hard with a pitchfork. This of course enraged the animal—as it would you or me—who delivered a great blow with his trunk, knocking the man unconscious. There's a chance he might not recover.[113]

Two parties have sprung up, one demanding that the elephant should be slain if the man dies, and the other side saying he mistreated the elephant and deserves his fate. You can guess which side I'm on! I went to see the elephant, and the pitchfork incisions are deep and red, but, rinsed and treated, are healing. So it was more than a prick, and must have hurt the elephant a great deal!

Mother is adding a bright yellow feather to this packet, in hopes you might identify its owner. She found it, of all places, on a snow mound in the Common. We wonder if it fell from a woman's hat, not from a bird overhead. One never knows these days.

Take care of yourself.

With love & affection, Cath

To Charles Pickering aboard the USS Vincennes
From Catharine Pickering, Boston

January 10, 1841

Cherished Cousin,

If our calculations are correct, the Squadron is back exploring the Sandwiches where the temperature must be nearly the opposite of Boston's.

Early this morning, the country carriages and sleds laden with hickory, pine, and walnut made their way slowly up Beacon Street, bound for the wood market, and as they passed, I heard that distinct crunching sound—the snow voice of winter. It shouts to the children of Beacon Hill, come out & play, the snow is a perfect consistency for sledding and snowballs and angel wings! Now it's afternoon, and energetic small bundles, accompanied by a parent or nanny, are running up the Common's hill and coasting down the long diagonal to Boylston Street, an exercise they repeat over and over despite the stinging cold.

Bountiful energy! Lucky children. They live happily in the moment—unburdened, save for wet mittens and snow down their boots!

Dr. Binney has organized a splendid new series on wildlife providers, and it began the other evening with Squire Waterton. Remember the popularity of his last book?—an account of his strange adventures while wandering barefoot in South America? Every seat was filled, people curious to see this naturalist whose eccentricities are renown: his stables in Yorkshire designed to allow his horses to talk to one another; his "Cure" pills and his pet birds; the nondescript head he fashioned so convincingly that some Londoners think it's the head of an Indian he murdered. It's said he's such a good taxidermist, he can bind two animal skins into one without anyone being the wiser.

A critic of Mr. Audubon, Squire Waterton—a handsome man with a high, broad brow—made no mention of the artist. Which was wise, given Boston's allegiance to Audubon. Yet he talked about birds the entire time, enchantingly so, almost as if posing as a rival. He's extremely sure of himself, nearly arrogant. Still, I liked him very much. His eccentricities remind me of Mr. Booth, the way he cares so deeply about the natural world, birds in particular.

"There are many people I do not love," he confessed, "but never have I met an animal I do not love, and birds especially win my affection. Ornithology is the natural science I most embrace, and over the years, after setting up an excellent telescope in my drawing room that is trained on the lake that surrounds Walton Hall, and the fields and forest on the opposite shore, I have followed every species my eye alights on, and with more rapt attention than I do my closest kin, except, of course, my beautiful wife.

"But after my father's death, there was less and less to observe. The wild birds kept declining, to the point of vanishing in some cases, particularly the larger ones. The raven, the kite, the buzzard—these and other kinds were being annihilated by ruthless gamekeepers. The new game laws aren't any good; they encourage this slaughter. Hunters, once they have their license, shoot just about every bird unfortunate enough to fly their way. The proprietors of museums are also responsible. The superb kingfisher, for example, was becoming scarce because curators wanted it for their collections. They offer such an attractive price that on the canals the watermen steer with an alert eye and a gun cocked beside them.

"To watch the lake and woodlands steadily draining of our friends—it would have broken my father's heart. It certainly was breaking mine. The property was becoming cheerless without their song, bland without their color, dull without their vivaciousness. Name me another creature that is so quick and animated and talkative when the sun is out. You can't, because there isn't one! Then something occurred to me. I would build a bird preserve! It has taken years to complete, but today Walton Hall's entire property is encircled by a high wall, and every advantage is given to birds inside its perimeter. Neither guests nor workers are permitted to use firearms. No boats are allowed on the lake during breeding time. Specially built towers give certain species—owls, jackdaws, and starlings—safe nesting sites. An abundance of seed and food for all creatures is left in many locations throughout the park.

"One friend made fun of the project. Birds, he predicted, were too dim-witted to know the difference between life on one side of the wall from life on the other side. Ah, but he's had to eat his words! I've recorded over 100 species within the park, with many a rarity seen, and they instinctively know they are safe. The kingfishers are back; the hawks and the ospreys are too. The herons are multiplying, free of the impish boys and vagabonds who once caught them. Last June I saw a remarkable sight: twenty-five herons suspended over the lake. Hundreds of bream had risen to the surface to bask in the sun's warmth, and the birds were trying to catch them. Herons aren't good divers—they usually get their fish by patiently wading along the banks—so it was a comical game of cat-and-mouse. When the herons swooped down to the surface, the fish were alerted by their shadows overhead and sank down a few feet. When the herons gave up and rose higher again, the fish rose back to the surface. Back and forth it went for hours!"[114]

Squire Waterton made his Park sound as desirable as Eden. He had huge respect for his father, a famous canal builder and sportsman in his day, and ended the evening with a barely credible story about him, which I'll save for another time. I just looked at the clock, and need to hurry & change. We are attending a play at the Warren tonight, and James landed front row seats.

With unwavering affection, Cath

SUMMER, 1895

Sophie, early in 1841 Charles and his *Vincennes* shipmates were in the midst of a rigorous survey of the Hawaiian islands. Charles, once again, was fascinated by the sight of a primitive race creeping in the direction of a civilized society. Take a look at his journal musings:[115]

We found Honolulu a much more considerable place than we anticipated, with several buildings in the European style, with cupolas, &c. There were 9 vessels in the harbour, mostly square-rigged. We have already visited with Mr. Couthouy, whose health is much improved and who has told us about many interesting sites I hope to visit. After only a few days, already I'm fairly well acquainted with Hawaiian vegetation and have filled my box with specimens several times.

I recently walked up to a prominent waterfall where, just above, streams are led off for irrigating the Valley. This was a new thing among the Polynesians, both the art & necessity—but in general all the cultivation that is carried on on the leeward sides of these islands is by means of irrigation. Taro forms the principal article, by means of artificial ponds, but there are also some Bananas, Sugar Cane, &c. In the gardens at Honolulu, ornamental trees & plants are watered from wells.

On the routes into town I constantly meet Natives bringing in wood and provisions of various kinds for the Market—and even charcoal-making is carried on up the Valley. This is the only place in these seas where we have found anything like a regular system of industry, or any organized adoption of the Customs of Civilized Society. I've spent considerable time walking among the Salt-ponds and am surprised at the extent to which the manufacture of salt from seawater is carried on. Salt is used to cure pork & fish, and the Natives are adept at the business, since they aren't adverse to salt provisions, which we found true on other islands. Salt is exported to Chile, to Oregon, Kamchatka and the Russian settlements, and some to California.

The canoes in use are much like the Taheitian, excavated from the trunk of a tree, & with an outrigger. The sail, when present, is much like that of the *Vincennes*. A native's needs are extremely modest. A little fish & poi, & he is content. This is regarded as one of the main obstacles to improvement. In some parts of these islands, a native can support himself for less than 2 cents per day, and needs very little to exist.

Licentiousness prevails throughout these islands. Formerly there was promiscuous intercourse; men living with several wives, &

women with several husbands. But since the operations of the missionaries, and the enactment of Marriage laws, there has been some improvement, although I was stuck with how few persons I met could be regarded as really paired! The Veneral disease is attributed to Cook's sailors and pervades the whole population due to the habits of the people.

The Diving Dress was used today to repair the copper on one of our ships, the Porpoise. It excited the curiosity of the whole town; & the wharves were crowded with Natives to witness the Operation. It occurs to me that, as more and more visitors come here, because Hawaiians are an attentive lot, it won't take them long to learn the technical tricks of more Civilized people.

"A little fish and a little poi, and they were content." That's how Cousin Charles later summed up the lives of the Hawaiian natives in his book *Races of Man*. Henry Thoreau in his journal referred to Charles' description, but, as was his nature, he was critical of the natives:

"A savage lives simply due to ignorance and idleness, whereas the philosopher lives simply due to wisdom."[116]

To Charles Pickering aboard the USS Vincennes
From Catharine Pickering, Boston

February 6, 1841

Dearest Cousin,

Capt. Couthouy is back among us. It was something of a shock to see him. He's aged ten years in the two he's been away, and shed so much weight, he was barely recognizable. Yet he is as boisterous as ever. The Creightons had a "nog" party for him last Sunday, after which Mother, Father, and I stole him away for supper at the Revere House.

How did the Expedition's artists keep up with the collecting process?

The Captain spoke with intensity while we watched the movements of his ruddy, whiskery face, as if it was a portal to those remote shores.

"They didn't!" he told us. "We had a stringent rule that any specimens hauled over the rail had to be drawn as quickly as possible. Especially the coral animals, because their forms and colors changed so fast. But the artists couldn't keep up, not even with help from the naturalists.

"One day off the Brazilian coast, I got the surprise of my life. It was flat calm—not a breath of air, not a ripple—and I was hauling a huge sheet of kelp over the side to examine the thalassina attached to it, and found myself staring down at the biggest crab I've ever seen. A monster lithodes. With its legs outstretched, it must have been over three feet in circumference. I brought it aboard to examine it, sketch it, and fix it for shipping, but within the hour Capt. Wilkes accused me of smelling up the ship with my collections and made me throw it back."

"No one will believe such a magnificent creature exists. What I would have given for that Frenchman's camera, especially when we got to the Coral Islands! My eyes, I swear, are bigger and rounder because of what we saw on those islands.

"The Corals fool you. They are indescribably beautiful from a distance, but, closer in, it can turn treacherous. Like the island of Tepoto, in the Disappointments. From our anchorage, the natives seemed receptive to our presence, but when we rowed to shore, and I jumped overboard, holding up trinkets while wading through the surf, they came running down the beach waving their spears! Not in a friendly way. The crew shot blank cartridges, but that made the islanders even angrier, and they kept coming, noisy, growling, and furious.

"They called us cowards for bearing firearms. Our interpreter distinctly heard them shouting: 'You white men are cowards! Brave men don't carry guns.'

"Aiming mustard seed at their legs finally made them scatter into the woods. But our Fleet was uneasy all night, with double the watchmen as usual. At dawn the next morning, we weighed anchor and hauled out of there. We learned from other ships that Tepoto's natives had been fired at by traders engaged in the pearl industry. There were injuries, perhaps deaths. No wonder they weren't thrilled to see us.

"A few days later we anchored in the shallows of Dog Island. Uninhabited and scarcely ever visited, it's as peaceful a paradise as any you can imagine. All kinds of creatures live there. As soon as we beached our boats, we bore witness to a sight that gave us a good laugh. A large crab was seized by a large snake, and then suddenly a stout bird flew down and seized them both! The island is so fat with nature, this culling must happen all the time.

"It was Dog's birds that most made us stare. They are so colorful, so full of song, so content and so remarkably tame. We took them in hand, or tipped them off their nests to reach their eggs. Barnyard fowl aren't half so tame. No guns have shattered their tranquility—and we had no desire to break the spell."[117]

When Father, Mother and I returned home, we looked for Dog Island on a whaler's chart but did not find it.

February 28, 1841

About our Salem neighbor, Mr. Hathorne. You'll be amused by what goes on in his barn—another example of animal intelligence.

Whenever Mr. Hathorne feeds his horse, six or more pigs make a visit to the stable and crowd around. He's never thought much about it. Pigs are social animals, and since Mr. Hathorne is one to talk to his animals, he expected the pigs liked the barn's social atmosphere. One day, after pouring feed into the trough, he looked down and saw one of the pigs rubbing the horse's knee with his snout, which caused the horse to start back and lose a mouthful of corn. The pigs darted forward and ate the grain before the horse had time to bite or kick them. Was their mischief premeditated? Apparently, for the pigs repeated the same behavior the very next day. However, this time the horse didn't react to the ringleader's snout on his knee, whereupon the pig took more drastic measures. It bit the horse in the leg, causing the poor horse to release a mouthful of grain.

Mr. Hathorne now shuts the pigs out of the barn when he feeds the horse. But when he feeds the pigs, he allows the horse to come by and share their grub. The pigs grunt with displeasure. His horse raises his lip over his teeth and grins.

February's "Snow Moon"—how aptly named by the Indians. We've had three blizzards in quick succession. Along Charles Street, the snow banks are so high, the sidewalks are more like tunnels. Oliver and his "little gang of thieves," as Mother refers to them, have set up an obstacle course that starts at the top of Chestnut, wraps around a series of chairs, and finishes on the flat. James has tried to photograph them, but their sleds go too fast.

James joins me in wishing you smooth sailing.

Much love, Catharine

Summer, 1895

The quantity of specimens that Charles and other Exploring Expedition naturalists collected and sent home boggles the mind. At Rio de Janeiro, their first-port-of-call below the Equator, they shipped roughly 50,000 items back to the States. By the end of the voyage, they had prepared, listed and shipped a staggering 40 tons of natural riches, including fossils and corals, seawater from every ocean, minerals from several mountains. In the bird department alone, they crated roughly 2,000 samples representing roughly 1,000 species.

They sent back miscellaneous items as well, such as an Aborigine cloak made from the skins of twenty-three opossums and rocks from the Hawaiian shore where Captain Cook was slain.

The first shipments were directed to Philadelphia. Then, in 1840, the receiving city changed to Washington. The Expedition's crates were hoisted up to the top floor of the newly constructed Patent Office, where a cabinet of curiosities already existed for objects as diverse as the femur of a Missouri mastodon and President Washington's knee-breeches. The Expedition's multitude of treasures would sit in a great clutter, until our cousin Charles, once he was home, accepted the challenge of serving as curator and put the clutter in order.

To Charles Pickering aboard the USS Vincennes
From Catharine Pickering, Boston

March-April 1841

Dearest Charles,

James gave a splendid lecture on the daguerreotype last night. Many of the women in the room now want to take up photography as a hobby. Such is his appeal!

Since Monsieur Daguerre's announcement nearly two years ago, surprisingly few Boston residents have mastered the art of image-making, and the hall was packed with beginners looking for instruction.[118] Years of working in his father's plating business and learning the skill of cladding candlesticks and lamps taught James a fair amount about chemical elements. It also taught him that when you work for the public, to be ready for anything—the woman, for instance, who wanted her deceased dog to be gold-plated no matter the cost!

After his father's business closed, he worked as a pension agent, hating every minute and yet amassing a fortune in record time, which allowed him to embark on his true calling, that of inventor. A beehive, a solar lamp, a sensible plough. He's too modest to say so, but he's had one success after another. Once he fastened onto photography, he made a mind-blowing discovery—bromine can greatly accelerate exposure time. Daguerre's early images took as long as ten minutes or more to develop; and now James has the process down to ten seconds. And his sitters look more alive than dead because of it. Unfortunately, a gentleman in Philadelphia made the same discovery and confiscated every ounce of bromine on the East Coast. So James has set out to find an alternative solution.

He displayed his photographs onto a large screen, and you should have heard the oohs and aahs. His images of Boston streets are some of the first! There's one of the new brick house on Louisburg Square, and off to one side is a dog's tail—just the tail. The rest of the dog is out of sight. The audience probably thought the tail was a mistake, but it was just James having fun.

He kept glancing my way. I admit, I didn't mind. Let Lydia Macomber and her minions spin their gossip. It's true what the poets say, the heart does skip a beat! Sometimes several.

I've told James so much about you, and now he, too, searches the papers each day for the smallest crumb of news concerning the Wilkes Expedition.

April 10th. The nation is in shock. President Harrison is dead, and only 31 days after his swearing in. Age 68, he was the oldest President to hold that office. But he had spunk and we thought he might accomplish at least a few great things. Dr. Parkman thinks his physicians never should have treated his pneumonia with leeches. Draining the body of its precious fluids, he feels, can do more harm than good. And yet the Wilkinsons credit bloodletting for their daughter's recovery from whooping cough. And Seth Williams says it cured his jaundice.

And Uncle Octavius, his hemorrhoids.

Please write your thoughts about leeches on the face of the moon. So I can receive them most expediently!

Wishing you smooth seas, your loving cousin.

To Charles Pickering aboard the USS Vincennes
From Catharine Pickering, Boston

May 4, 1841

Dearest Charles,

The Public Garden opened for the season on May 1ˢᵗ and most every family on the Hill joined the ceremonies. What a festive crowd! The sun shone brightly, the Brigade Band played mightily, and children were as plentiful as June bugs, climbing trees, playing tag and trampling the flower beds with scarlet-faced Mr. Teschemacher in hot pursuit. The only ink blot was the sight—and it was an awful sight—of many more bonnets adorned with feathers than last year. Reverend Peabody is right. Feathers are becoming much too fashionable, and one can't help but wonder how much the trend is impacting the bird population.

Lucinda and I have met several times to discuss how to raise interest in a committee to protect birds. Meanwhile, we write down every species we catch sight of in parks and along the river. Some say the city's noise and commotion scares birds away. But they can't be looking very hard. I counted 33 robins feeding at the parade ground one morning in early March. By mid-March, the song sparrows were everywhere & singing, and kept on singing through two late snowstorms. What optimists! Our list of migrants and locals keeps lengthening. Recently, Father and I heard a cuckoo near the bandstand who, hunt as we might, never showed himself.

"It's going to rain!" said Father. It actually did, in a day or two.

Just as you predicted, English sparrows are on the rise, and so is their chasing of other birds. Lucinda recently saw the opposite—a hummingbird chasing an English sparrow across Beacon Street and to the roof of Mr. Gray's Conservatory!

"It was a wonderful sight for patriotic eyes," she laughed.[119]

Not much escapes her. The papers recently shared the Duke of Argyll's claim that no bird can fly backwards. "Apparently, hummingbirds aren't sticking with this. I've seen at least one hummingbird backing out of a lily's trumpet—and quite handily!"

May 15, 1841

On the motion of Dr. Storer, it was voted that Dr. Binney will recommend to the Secretary of the Navy that a portion of the Exploring Expedition's collections be set aside for our Museum. Father and Uncle Octavius are delighted with this decision, as you will be. Mr. Couthouy meanwhile keeps donating objects from his journey. Just yesterday: two eggs of the Frigate bird, which no other collection in the country possesses. Also, several rare shells from Terra del Fuego. It's unclear how these objects arrived in Boston, on which ship. No one is asking, for it's unlikely that Mr. Couthouy got Capt. Wilkes's permission to have them sent.

Here at #75 Beacon, everything's a-jumble. Since moving here, Mother and Father have felt terribly distant from their friends on Franklin Street, so the trunks are being repacked for a return to our old neighborhood. I think it's all the trains in the distance, they make a lot of noise, as does the street traffic. A newly built house awaits us on Tontine Crescent, with its own yard and trellis.

My daily bird-watching outings to the Common and Garden will keep on. It's amusing, really, the glances I get. I'll be watching the sky, only to discover that I, myself, am being watched! Apparently, a man with a gun looking up at the sky is quite normal. But for a woman to gaze upward with no gun, no apparent reason—oh, I must be losing my mind!

The other day I was watching a shape high up in the old copper beech when Mr. Thackery walked by.

"So, Miss Pickering, what do you see?" His brow was furrowed, his mouth downturned.

"A golden-crowned thrush!"

"Really?" Suddenly he was alert with interest. He craned his neck, but he was looking in the wrong direction. "A shame, *that* law," the law that prohibits guns in the park.

"One cannot get to know a bird when it's alive, by sight? without turning it into a specimen?" I asked. "Guns are lazy—quite a stupid invention."

At that moment he looked at me as if through crosshairs.

"Good evening, Miss Pickering."

"And to you, Mr. Thackery."

To Charles Pickering aboard the USS Vincennes
From Catharine Pickering, Boston

June 12, 1841

Dearest Cousin,

Your shipmate George Tuttle recently paid the Society a visit. He has fully recovered from the illness that cut short his time on *Vincennes*. His descriptions were riveting! Those two killer whales off New Zealand, their massive jaws locked in combat.[120] And the sun and the moon hanging like huge saucers over opposite horizons in those same waters, a sight that gave him goose-bumps.

He spoke of Capt. Wilkes' indebtedness to you for the countless hours you spend identifying specimens and preparing them for shipment. The pains you take is no surprise to us; you've always worked yourself to the bone. But we're concerned for your well-being. Mr. Tuttle said your stateroom is lined with specimens, some in, some out of cages—live and dead birds, frogs, geckos, snakes, fish eggs and whale teeth, seeds & pods & potted ferns—and that when the wind picks up, and the boat heaves, jars break and cages open, and the smell can be so overpowering, you are forced to sleep on deck.

Please take care of yourself. We are counting on you to return home in one piece.

By our reckoning, the *Vincennes* is nearing the entrance to the Columbia River. To step foot on American soil—what a relief that will be, even though you will still be a great distance from home.

June 18, 1841

It's been an unusual twenty-four hours. My respect for Dr. Binney continues to climb, especially his advice to not forsake the ordinary for the bizarre, and here's why:

Mr. Kimball's Boston Museum at the corner of Tremont and Bromfield opened with a colorful, jammed gala last week, and who travelled up from New York for the occasion but our acquaintance Mr. Phineas Barnum. The curls on his head must spring from some internal combustion, he's so full of nervous energy! Earlier in the day, he stopped by the Society to inspect our contents. The two-headed snake is back in its case, and he told Dr. Binney he'd pay a handsome sum for it should it ever be for sale.[121] Later, we strolled down to the wharves, to look for shark bills for his collection, and the whole time he chattered like a wound-up toy about his sudden interest in obtaining two-headed snakes and the likes.

Scudder's American Museum has been losing money since the death of Mr. Scudder, and your friend would like to acquire it.[122] He wondered how Boston's museums were faring. What were our chief expenses, and how generous were our members? He wants to take Scudder's in the direction of more intrigue, more diversity. Although he has barely two coins to rub together, he's sure his plan will attract investors. Putting Old Joice Heth on display, he said, had taught him a thing or two, notably that the average Joe's curiosity for rare sights is unquenchable and that exhibiting oddities rakes in the coins.

No doubt about that! In our town, it seems the more serious and educational the exhibit, the less it fetches. Whereas if a giant clam with eyes and ears went on display, its exhibitors would be able to build a staircase to the moon on the money made.

Down on the wharves, with the sun warming our backs, Mr. Barnum was disarmingly honest. "The trick," he confided, "is to goad the public's curiosity in any way possible!" He let drop that Doctor Warren had a hand in the Joice Heth hoax. But I think what probably happened was that the Doctor lent credibility to Mr. Barnum's scheme without intending to.

SUMMER, 1895

Sophie, a few words about the once-famous Joice Heth, who caused a great sensation in her day. Why was she famous? Because of her fantastic age of 161 years, or so P.T. Barnum widely advertised. I have a faint, awful memory of the time Barnum exhibited the old woman in Boston, and to this day I'm still surprised my parents fell for the charade and lined up with the rest of the world, paying exorbitantly for tickets to see her.[123]

Barnum acquired the negress in the winter of 1834-35. At the time, he was out of work, with a wife and daughter to support, and, rascal that he was, he realized that Joice Heth could be molded into a money-making sensation. Her skin was so pasty and translucent that she looked positively ancient. She was blind, toothless, partly paralyzed, and thin and wrinkled as a snake.

Barnum advertised that when she'd been a slave of Augustine Washington, she had raised his son, George Washington, from birth. It helped that she was a talkative soul and had lots to say on any question put to her, whether it was about little George or the red-coats of the Revolutionary War. Doctor Warren was one of several physicians invited by Barnum to a private showing, and, after examining Heth, although the doctor came away less than half convinced, like the others he wondered if she possibly could be as old as Barnum claimed, and conniving Barnum used the doctor's uncertainty to his advantage.

Barnum was a brilliant marketer, because he lied so effortlessly. Previously, when the exhibit had opened in New York at Niblo's Garden, he had the newspapers eating out of the palm of his hand.

"Joice Heth is the greatest curiosity in the world," ran *The Morning Herald*.

"Her appearance is much like an Egyptian mummy just escaped from its sarcophagus," *The New York Evening Star* sang out.

"Here is the first person to dress the infant who led us to freedom!" exclaimed *The Tribune*.

Thousands flocked to Niblo's in the first two weeks. When the lines began to shorten, Barnum gave New York a rest and brought Joice Heth to other cities, including Boston.

Here, too, tickets sold faster than hotcakes. When the curiosity-seekers were satisfied and attendance began to slacken, that's when a conspicuous letter from "a Visitor" turned up in a Boston paper. The anonymous tipster claimed that Joice Heth was not a living-and-breathing soul after all, but fabricated of India rubber, whalebone and springs, and that her voice belonged to her exhibitor, a ventriloquist.

Crafty Barnum! A fresh wave of interest grabbed the city, and folks who had already seen Joice Heth wanted to re-examine her. How had they been so deceived? Others who hadn't—my parents were among them—were eager to inspect this mechanical doll that had fooled everyone with its realness. But as soon as our eyes fell on her, it was obvious that Joice Heth was flesh and blood. To a seven-year-old boy, although she looked positively ancient, she clearly was made of living material. To this day, the memory of her—her blind white eyes, her warped four-inch fingernails, her wiry white hair—still makes me shiver.

Barnum wrung every cent he could from exhibiting the poor old woman, who in actuality was in her eighties. Her act allowed him to test the waters.

It was merely a prelude for everything to come. Once he became proprietor of the New York Museum, his gimmicks would soar to new heights.

June 18, 1841 letter continued...

Mr. Kimball claims that his Boston Museum is for the whole family, and that he has excluded any objects that could be construed as objectionable. I don't entirely agree.

At the opening, James and I, joined by Mr. Barnum, covered every inch of the new building. It is located at the corner of Tremont and Bromfield, only a few doors down from our Natural History doorway. There's a spacious auditorium on the top floor, and we were headed up the staircase in that direction when we reached the Feejee Mermaid on the second floor, and Mr. Barnum came to an abrupt halt.[124] Capt. Eades' son sold the mermaid to Mr. Kimball for a song, and the grisly object now sits in its own glass case. There's plenty of other hokum in Mr. Kimball's museum—two sphinx eggs, the skeleton of Europe's elusive species of barnacle geese that grow on trees, a talking hen, an elephant's solid gold trunk—but the mermaid has the seat of honor. Or, should I say, the seat of horror!

I found the mermaid so repulsive, I stood at a distance, but Mr. Barnum came right up to the glass and stared in awe.

"Remarkable!" he murmured.

"A remarkable sham!" countered James.

"Ah, sir, don't you feel it? wonder for the unknown!"

"Real objects can inspire greater wonder."

"A king in the Middle Ages possessed a mirror that magically could reflect his enemies approaching from far away. True? False? Does it matter?" asked Mr. Barnum. "I purchased the mirror and it's on display in a glass box, and everyone asks, 'If only I could hold it, would I see my enemies?' It fascinates them."

As we continued touring the museum, Mr. Barnum doubled back for another look at the mermaid. Was Mr. Kimball willing to part with her? Yes, he was willing, but for the right price.

The next morning the two men met with Francis Gray, the naturalist. Mr. Barnum didn't really care if the mermaid was a coupling of species or the real thing, but he thought he'd make at least one attempt to know its derivation.

"There's not the slightest trace of stitching between the monkey head and the fish body," observed Mr. Gray. "The spine runs unbroken from the lower body up to the base of the skull, and my microscope reveals fish scales beneath the hair of the shoulders. And yet this, er, thing is manufactured."

"Why do you say that?" asked Mr. Barnum.

"Because I don't believe in mermaids," said Mr. Gray.

"Very well. But the absence of suspicious underpinnings gives me every reason to purchase this artifact!" exclaimed Mr. Barnum. And with that, he and Mr. Kimball settled on a fair price. The mermaid's new owner said he would send instructions for its delivery.

Mr. Barnum doesn't hide his deceptive leanings. Maybe that's a strength, not to pretend that you are doing anything but pretending. The last I saw of him, he was headed toward the train station swinging two suitcases—one of which, I happen to know, contained the curled skin of a boa constrictor—and whistling "Yankee Doodle."

Oh, to be so untroubled and ready for anything!

SUMMER, 1895

Well, Sophie, P.T. Barnum was one helluva go-getter, and it didn't take him long to raise the cash and purchase the museum of his dreams, the American Museum. It wasn't until the next summer, the summer of 1842, that Moses Kimball took it upon himself to personally deliver the dried-up, atrocious-looking mermaid to the showman in New York, who immediately got busy publicizing its debut. Letters spaced strategically apart in three newspapers announced that a Dr. Griffin of the Lyceum of Natural History in London would be in town exhibiting a most noteworthy creature, a preserved mermaid he had recently bought from some Chinamen who had procured it in the Fiji Islands. In the meantime, a friend of Barnum's, posing as Dr. Griffin, showed the mermaid to a small circle of gentlemen in Philadelphia, which began a flurry of interest that radiated outward. With the letters now circulating in New York papers, and newsboys hawking pamphlets about the mermaid, curiosity over the mermaid reached the boiling point. Overnight, Barnum's museum became the public's favorite destination.

Around the country, more and more mermaids went on display. All were composites of different animals glued or sewed together. The original mermaid, which Mr. Kimball repurchased in 1859, ended up back in Boston looking more gruesome than ever. For the sake of Boston's impressionable children, thank heavens it is no longer on display. Let's hope it was buried a mile underground.

To Charles Pickering aboard the USS Vincennes
From Catharine Pickering, Boston

July 20, 1841

Dear Cousin,

Your latest letter says that if all goes well, you'll be home by next spring. We're already counting the days! After this packet goes out, I won't send any more letters into the yonder-blue, but will save them for your return, not trusting their slow transport by ship. Which reminds me of this news: The English have begun affixing a postage stamp to each letter to pay its freight. It's a slip of paper about the size of a thumb print, illustrated with Queen Victoria's profile, with a glutinous wash on its back. It's quite ingenious! And several of our statesmen are pressing Congress to adopt a similar measure.

Summer has been busy, to the point of breathlessness. We've had a series of guests in Salem—a few, boring beyond belief. But the company has been good for mother's health. I regularly ride the train into Boston, to the L'Histoire Society, the opposite of boring. Yesterday, Daniel Johnston brought in a great collection of lizards, and a Mainer deposited a stunning tourmaline crystal.

Since its doors opened, Mr. Kimball's Boston Museum has been all the rage, which doesn't seem quite fair. While it has some serious content— paintings and statues, as well as relics from the old Linnaean Society that went to Mr. Greenwood's Museum, all now found at Mr. Kimball's—it mostly caters to the bizarre and inexplicable. Our institution leans in the opposite direction, and, I suspect, will always be seen as too serious and studious to ever be wildly popular. Many Bostonians don't even know we exist, and, aside from naturalists, visiting out-of-towners rarely darken our door. They pay twice as much at Mr. Kimball's to see the Indian giant, when several of our cabinets have no equal in the museum world. It's terribly discouraging, the vapidness of humanity.

July 29, 1841

Four years is a long time to be away. Just to prepare you, while you've been gone, temperance has been growing in Boston, while abolitionism would if it could. Father and most of his friends ignore the former and favor the latter. For a stodgy city, Boston is pretty good about embracing the less fortunate. Then there are individuals like Mr. Appleton, who casually remarked to our librarian the other day that "a crazy-headed abolitionist is worse than the smallpox or yellow fever." James happened to be in the library doing some research. Overhearing this remark, he took the bait quite happily.

"Well then," he said to Mr. Appleton, "if you want to avoid being infected by a crazy-headed abolitionist, you'd better hurry out of this room. Quickly now!"

Mr. Appleton looked around so fast at James, his monocle fell out. He hadn't seen him sitting there in one of the coveys. It took no more than a few seconds for him to replace his monocle and flee the library!

SUMMER, 1895

Sophie, the news would soon ripple from one end of the continent to the other.

On July 18, 1841, while attempting to enter the Columbia River, the Exploring Expedition's ship *Peacock* struck a sandbar. There was no loss of life—human life, that is. However, the entire collection of scientific treasures on board, most dead but some alive, was lost, and lamentably this included Titian Peale's hundreds of bird specimens from the Hawaiian Islands and his treasured group of roughly 375 butterfly species as well as most of the Expedition's collected insects.

Among Peale's birds were several specimens of the honey eater, Moho nobilis. They were tremendously prized by Hawaiians, because, in contrast to their predominately glossy blackness, they had bright yellow tufts of feathers on their wings, which the natives sewed into royal robes, capes, and special ornaments. So valued were these birds, especially for their yellow tufts, that the Hawaiians trapped them, plucked out their brilliant feathers, and then released them so that they might regrow those decorative tufts.

Unfortunately, this catch-and-release strategy wasn't enforced. Charles made note in his journal that, in 1841, the "o-o"—the Moho nobilis—was already a rare sight. I've checked into this further, and the bird has all but disappeared from those islands by now.

Fall 1841

Dear Cousin,

The chill air has arrived, and with it an influenza that has interrupted daily life for many households, ours included. I'm recovering, but slowly.

Capt. Couthouy just returned from Washington, dejected and cross. How could anyone blame him. He meant to start the job of classifying the mollusks and shells that already have arrived from the Expedition, only to find his vast collection upended. A handler at the National Institution, with no scientific knowledge, noticed the tinfoil tags on each specimen had begun to whiten the alcohol in each jar, so he removed them, put them together in one big jar, and never thought to replace them. Without proper identification, the samples are useless, and so are Capt. Couthouy's notes. If that wasn't enough bad luck, his drawings have inexplicably vanished. Officials have been put on high alert to treat future shipments with the utmost care.

The Society's conchology committee, feeling the Captain's pain, have asked him into their fold. I saw him yesterday and he's developed a bad limp. What happened? I asked. "Losing all my specimens—it was like someone shot a cannon at me and I got it in the leg." Our friend really is in emotional tatters right now.

It doesn't seem to matter that firearms are prohibited in parts of the city. Like shadows, they slip under doorways and steal into places once considered safe.

Steel yourself. Last week our beloved shopkeeper Mr. Hodgkin died in the most senseless way. He was the victim of a deliberate shooting near the Court House, his lifeless body found lying against the curbstone in a pool of blood. A customer who argued with him over a trifle is missing and presumed guilty. Mr. Hodgkin's wife and two children have taken over managing the store. Their eyes are red with crying, poor things.

Here's more news from our Salem neighbor. It isn't exactly a Troc'ulus, but close enough.

Mr. Hathorne ventured out early one evening with his dog Medor to fetch a bird he'd seen earlier that lay wounded near the river, and while cutting through Broad Field, in the fading light he saw two bucks bent in fierce combat—a common enough sight in fall. Usually if a human or a dog approaches, they stop their feud and gallop off. So Mr. Hathorne was surprised that Medor's barking didn't cause their separation. He walked closer, close enough to see that the horns of the two animals had locked together. If they had begun in combat, now they were desperate to part, so desperate that as human and dog drew closer, they toppled over, righted themselves, toppled again, and then stood again.

The situation worsened when they rolled down an embankment and, at the bottom, were so entangled, they couldn't stand. Each had a wild look in its eye and was breathing hard. Stepping even closer, Mr. Hathorne noticed that one animal's antler had developed a hook that had virtually snapped onto the other's rack. He tried to break the horn, without success. Fearing for their necks and spines, he ran to his barn for a saw. Once back, he cut off the troublesome antler, whereupon free of each other, the bucks thundered into the woods, seeming no worse for wear.

When Mr. Hathorne went to look for the injured bird, it was gone.

SUMMER, 1895

Sophie Bear, I found this bill of lading with Cath's letters. It represents just one shipment of hundreds that the Exploring Expedition's sailors sent home. This particular delivery, transported by the schooner *Palestine*, arrived round the time that Captain Couthouy made the awful discovery that his large trove of mollusks and shells was in complete and utter disarray.

"Twenty-five boxes and ten barrels of shells; twenty-five boxes and one barrel of botanical and other specimens; seven boxes containing curiosities from Fiji Islands; one box containing seeds and roots and eight boxes containing coral; one box containing Deep Sea water. One Fiji drum; thirty-six bundles and one box containing spears and clubs; one box containing wheat; one box containing flower seeds; one box containing log books; one box containing books for philological department; one box containing a sleigh."

One has to wonder. How big a sleigh?

Nov-Dec 1841

Dear Charles,

Lucinda and I have decided to wait until spring before buttonholing members for our new organization. "The New England Society for Protecting Birds," we are calling it. Warmer weather and the flutter of wings, we hope, will be our best advertisement. Meanwhile, our list of local bird sightings continues to grow, with the recent addition of a painted bunting. Mr. Howard confirmed that a painted bunting this far north is a rare sight. It was James who glimpsed the bird, a "flying rainbow" he calls it, in the vicinity of Swallow's Pond!

There's a dispute in progress, and it likely will still be roiling once you're home, so here's a bit of explanation. It's over bird waste—yes, bird dung! It's a silly quarrel. Although it isn't entirely.

Some Boston merchants—Wadsworth Cabot among them—have a plan to import guano from the Chincha Islands. The English have been hauling guano back to home waters for a couple of years. You know their claim, that it doubles a farmer's yield of hay. You must have passed those rainless islands and their snowy hills of guano as the *Vincennes* sailed up the Peruvian coast. Another group, which has the support of Rev. Peabody, Mr. Teschemacher and the harbormaster, vehemently opposes retrieving guano from the Chinchas, saying that the waste has been accumulating since before humans drew breath, and that Nature should be left alone.

Mr. T. nevertheless enthusiastically supports guano taken from local sites. He did a test and found that his guanoed corn planted in late May ripened sooner than corn planted with regular manure on May First.

The two parties aired their differences at a public meeting. Noisily, I must say. It felt a little like lion warfare. Mr. Teschemacher argued that the

British were throwing colonies of marine birds on the Chincha Islands into pandemonium; and hunting them as well.[125] Heed the Incas! he implored. Their laws demanded that any Indian who hurt those birds, or stepped foot on the islands during rearing season, faced execution.

The birds were sacred to the Incas. They were proof of a loving God, to the extent that even their excrement was sacred and part of His plan.

Amen!

December 10, 1841

Young Henry Thoreau, it turns out, has a humorous side. What a surprise! I will have to tell Mr. Chase that "Hank the Crank" sometimes can turn into "Hank the Prank."

He came in last Tuesday and plunked down a box with five snake skins and a very unusual tortoise shell on my desk. Then he took a sizeable arrowhead out of his pocket and acted out how he and his brother found it while roaming the countryside.[126] We were the only ones in the gallery, so I expect he felt freer to put on this show.

"John and I started searching for Indian relics last fall. Our first time out, we found two arrowheads and then a pestle. We resumed our search one Sunday evening, when we strolled to the brow of the hill that overlooks Swampbridge Brook. It was a beautiful evening, the sky streaked with color that gave the trees an orange glow, and I felt so inspired by the ancient ground upon which we stood, that I broke into an extravagant tribute to those savage times."

Stretching tall, Henry swept one arm out over an invisible landscape and repeated his incantation in a booming voice:

"Oh, brother, how sacred this land! How often the Indians stood on this very spot and pondered the day's successes! Communed with the spirits of their forefathers! Watched the red sun set behind yonder woods! Welcomed the powerful moon! Worshipped the stars and applauded their glitter! Chanted verse to the deities-of-the-night until the first light of dawn. Right here where I'm standing, the mighty Chief Tahattawan once stood. Look! Here's an arrowhead for proof!

"I bent down to pull up the first stone my eye fell on and was flabbergasted to find a perfect arrowhead in my hand, as sharp as if it had been chiseled yesterday!"

Thoreau threw back his head and howled like a mirthful wolf.

His friends claim that Henry has uncanny luck for finding arrowheads, and from the many he's left at the Society, it would seem he does. Dr. Binney notes that it can't be luck alone that guides him, but rather his deep knowledge of native tribes and their territories.

Here's a small Troc'ulus to leave you with, dear cousin. Twenty-five years ago, Timothy Penniman of Salem found a turtle in his garden which is a short ways from his pond. With his penknife he marked the date and his initials on its shell, then forgot about the turtle. Travel forward to a day last summer when Mr. Penniman, now white-haired and hunchbacked, was working the same parcel. A movement caught his eye. Sidling toward him was the same shelled creature with TP on its back to identify it. Mr. Penniman was so overcome with emotion that he sat down next to his old friend and wept. He spotted the turtle several more times until colder weather set in and the turtle descended back down into the mud's warmer depths.

"What a gift that was, to see him again, while we're both still here," Mr. Penniman told Father. "He's a lot like me. He had the whole world to explore but liked it just fine where he was."[127]

A turtle was discovered in South Carolina with the date 1802 engraved on its back, but Mr. Penniman's turtle is striking because it turned up so close to where he first saw it. Normally I want the days to go by slowly. But now it's fine if they gallop as we wait for you to be safely back. Then they must slow down again!

With affection, Cath

SUMMER, 1895

Sophie, do yourself a favor and stop by the New England Museum of Natural History on Berkeley Street, as the Society is now called, and feast your eyes on Henry Thoreau's collection of natural marvels.[128] When Thoreau died in 1862, the Society was a chief recipient of his cherished objects, which included over one-thousand pressed New England plants, a considerable trove of bird nests and eggs, a one-of-a-kind shell of a Blandings tortoise, and a trunk of Indian relics. Included in the trunk's contents is an impressive arrowhead labelled "Tahattawan" that rests inside a large oyster shell for safekeeping.[129]

Despite her faltering health, Cath did her best to remain a loyal correspondent. But as you can see, over time her letters were becoming thinner and thinner, just as she was.

⸺ ๑ ⸺

January 1842

Dear Charles,

The morning is overcast, and I feel the same. I know Mary has written to you about my illness. I'm not interested in elaborating, except to say how boring it is that lethargy has the upper hand on these clear, crisp winter days. I try to conserve energy for the occasional outing with James and family. Even then, I'm apt to crawl home early.

But last evening James and I attended a talk by Mr. Teschemacher that left me energized. It was on the progress of science.[130] Some people feel the sciences have added so much detail and gotten so complicated, it's impossible for ordinary people to follow them. But if they were on the inside track, said Mr. T., they'd see things differently. The more facts are gathered, dissolving the clouds of error and ignorance, the more science's great lump of clay is being divided into sub-divisions, and sub-sub-divisions, making a subject easier to grasp. He believes the days of one person trying to embrace every little detail about the natural world are nearly over. For who, he points out, can possibly master an entire dictionary by heart?

You can. But few others are so driven!

The overworked naturalist will disappear—that's Mr. Teschemacher's prediction—and his labors will gradually be taken over by specialists. The botanist, the conchologist, the ornithologist, the ichthyologist, the geologist, and still others whose fields aren't yet defined. Mr. T. envisions specialists for trees, for ocean currents, for microbes, and even for the moon, the stars, and the blackness between. It's going to take all kinds of scientists, he predicts, to fathom the inner invisible and the outer invisible.

Mr. Burns, the banker, raised an interesting question. What's the point of knowing so much?

"We won't know until we know," Mr. T replied. "Certain rewards, however, are already obvious. Consider the gifts of two of our members, Mr. Audubon and Reverend Peabody, who have introduced us to the birds of our neighborhoods. And consider what the Exploring Expedition is sending us—exotic species to be displayed in our museums. Will a more intimate knowledge of wild creatures replace the urge to shoot and destroy them? Perhaps."

Elwood Carter of Brooksville, Maine, gave the Museum one of the most unusual mammals we've ever seen, an Indian's dog thought to be a cross between a wolf and a fox. A Penobscot Indian gave it to Elwood's grandfather. It's so expertly preserved & stuffed, it looks alive. We've placed it in the reading room, and it stops people in their tracks.

There's this news from the *Courier*. A massive Mammoth has been discovered encased in ice in Siberia. Its head alone weighs 414 pounds; its tusks, 360 pounds. Father is a recent convert to the theory that the climate in northern regions once was significantly warmer, until a stunning change took place and fierce cold descended, dooming large animals like the Mammoth. Mr. Agassiz is signed up to lecture on the great Ice Age that blanketed northern Europe when he's next in Boston.[131] The rumor persists that he intends to relocate here.

SUMMER, 1895

Sophie, when the sun's out and the corn is growing fast, it makes a popping noise. The same can be said about the sciences during the mid-1800s. The sun was out and the sciences were popping!

Boston was fertile ground for the scientific revolution that was taking place. Its maritime industry, its halls of learning, its centers of medicine all contributed to the popping noise, the growth and breakout of different scientific disciplines.

Naturalists like our Charles studied all three of Nature's fiefdoms—plants, animals, and minerals. The more they collected, the more the blurry field of "natural history" yielded sub-groups. Ichthyology, ornithology, mammalogy, conchology, herpetology, and, coined by the mid-1800s, "biology." A narrow focus gave a researcher half a chance of making discoveries about a species within the fold of its genus. Eventually, the naturalist, an amateur, would fade from view as specialists took over. Had Charles been born a few decades later, he likely would have narrowed his sights and specialized in botany, or maybe anthropology or ornithology. Instead, born in 1805, he belonged to the era of the generalist. A jack-of-all trades, so-to-speak. It didn't hurt that he had a Pickering's surplus energy for scaling Nature's enormities. It paid off, and quite literally, since he was one of the first men of science to live off his wages, to be paid for being curious.

The more specimens collected, the more species were identified, the more specialists were hired to study them, the more laboratory space was adopted, and the more museum space was needed for preserving and displaying natural treasures.

Obscurities in Nature lay everywhere. America's first full-time scientists rushed forth to tease out the innermost secrets of plants and animals. There were no easy answers, however. And, to digress, there still aren't! You've met my friend, the biologist Francis Herrick. He spent an entire year investigating a lobster's claw, expecting to find a store of inner embryonic cells that could shed light on a lobster's ability to replace its claw. But his search revealed nothing, and he's back at square one.

January 30, 1842

Dear Charles,

Such a surprise encounter I had today! I've just returned home from the Society from a delightful hour spent with Charles Dickens, and am sitting down to write you while the details are fresh in my mind. Yes, Mr. Boz! He's as charming as a prince. A ladies' man, I'd say.

Boston has been in a drunken state ever since the steamship carrying the author and his wife docked at Long Wharf on Saturday.[132] There's a tremendous crowd outside the Tremont House, and it isn't likely to disperse until their visit is over. Everyone and his cousin hope for a glimpse of Mr. Dickens. Our family has been extremely lucky in that regard. Father, Mother and Mary attended a welcoming dinner for the couple at Papanti's Hall, which preceded a special performance at the Tremont Theatre of *Nicholas Nickleby*.

Father had the honor of sitting next to Mrs. Dickens, a handsome woman whose calm disposition is so different from her husband's nervous & excitable nature. Her husband's hand aches, she confided, due to people shaking it "like madmen." Mr. Dickens has had to hire a secretary to help him answer the hundreds of invitations he receives each day. And requests. Several ladies have requested a lock of hair!

I had no pep that evening and missed the performance, but mother said the theater was filled to the rafters. The audience stood and gave thunderous hurrahs when Mr. and Mrs. entered their box.

Fate nevertheless intervened this morning. I was cataloguing new objects when a voice rang out. "Great Scott! What a monster!" Pictures of Mr. Dickens pave the newspapers, so the attractive man emerging from the stairwell was at once familiar. It was high noon, and his holler was in reaction to the bright sun barreling through the tall windows and projecting an immense shadow of the bronze rhinoceros sculpture onto the far wall. The only other patron I've known to notice the immense shadow is James!

He asked to be shown our collection of sandstone-embedded bird-foot marks, which we keep in a special set of drawers.

Astonishing! Out of this world! he exclaimed.

Mr. Dickens is so animated, he appears ready to jump over the moon. I've heard his father was a great exaggerator. The same trait resides in the son. His every movement, his every word carries a bit of excess. And the colorful stories he has stored away—they leap out in conversation as much as they do on to paper, I discovered.

Dr. Binney, who had been detained downstairs, joined us, accompanied by another guest, Benjamin Silliman. Solemn and dignified, the chemist from New Haven is anything but a silly man. (Father tells me that after he graduated from college, Prof. Silliman did a brief stint in Dr. Jackson's Boston laboratory. It truly is a small world.) His dark eyes bore into you; and when he speaks, his brow seems to bulge with voluminous thoughts. He was in town at the request of the Mayor, who is seeking his advice about the city's new public water system. Which bodies of water might be the best sources? Do the microscopic animalcules in ponds pose a risk to the health of residents who will be drinking those waters?

Author Dickens and chemist Silliman knew of one another but hadn't met before. It was a bit like watching Literature shaking hands with Science.

After a vigorous handshake—the vigor, I noticed, came mostly from Mr. Dickens' hand—the two locked into conversation, while Dr. Binney and I stood idly by, two posts content to listen to two pillars.

"Yes," said Mr. Dickens, "my wife and I are very comfortable at the Tremont House. London has scarcely anything like its plumbing. Eight water closets on the ground floor! And bathing-rooms in the basement! What a luxury! But tell me, Professor, is the tap alright to drink from?"

"Drink away, Mr. Dickens."

"But what of those animalcules? It's alarming to know we swallow hundreds in every gulp."

"Thousands, actually. But they are perfectly harmless, no need for concern," said Prof. Silliman with a shrug. "You've been swallowing them since birth, don't forget."

"What do they look like? Would I be frightened if they appear in my dreams?"

"Under a microscope—very diminutive shrimp."

"Are they in rainwater?"

"Oh my yes."

"Snow water?"

"Most definitely."

"Well water too?"

"It teems with them. But I promise, they'll do you no harm. Now allow me, author Dickens, to find out about you. What brings you to this fine institution?"

"*Extinction!*" Mr. Dickens said immediately. (His manner of speech is as rapid-fire as Prof. Silliman's is slow and ponderous.) "Bones of the bear dog; foot marks of lapsed birds; eggs of the near-extinct Auk. I am on an errand for a dear friend in England, the fossil hunter Mary Anning, the carpenter's daughter who has won a name for herself, deservedly so. Since she was a scruffy child, she has scoured the sea-cliffs on our southern coast and brought to light verterberries and other bones of mysterious monsters that are part dragon, part fish, part bird, part croc, depending on the skeleton, creatures that Miss Anning humbly advises are no longer swimming, walking, sliding, or flying because something demolished their kind a long, long time ago. Her theory has caused people to falsely accuse her of being an uneducated assuming person, for doesn't everybody know that when Earth was created, its creatures, divine works of God, were incapable of dying away, and that every original creature that walked the Earth upon its creation still walks the Earth today?!"

Mr. Dickens gulped down some air and continued.

"Distinguished Scientifics as well as pompous professors"—evidently the author had forgotten he was talking to one—"are beginning to come around and agree with Miss Anning. The strange monsters whose bones she has unearthed represent races of animals that no longer draw breath or replicate. Knowing I would be in a city whose captains have brought back ancient relics from every sea and shore, I wrote to Miss Anning saying I'd investigate Boston's museums for other instances of extinct creatures, for they serve as a cautionary tale. Don't shoot too many rabbits for your stew, for they might go the way of the Plesiosaurus!"[133] Mr. Dickens laughed heartily at his own witticism.

I wonder how Mrs. Dickens survives Mr. Dickens' frenetic personality. Rather than be married to him, I'd rather hold his stories quietly in my lap!

Mr. Dickens and Prof. Silliman walked back to the Tremont House together. That was the last I saw of the famous Londoner, although Father encountered him a few evenings later at a dinner at the Tuckermans, where Mr. Dickens read from *Old Curiosity Shop*. He had a bit too much ale that evening and several hands accompanied him back to the hotel. They wrapped a scarf around his head so that no one idling about in the lobby would recognize Mr. Boz and nothing harmful would surface in the morning paper.

Father has the greatest esteem for all Dr. Silliman has done to bring science out of the backwaters. His writing of the first scientific paper on a meteorite. His founding of the first scientific journal. There's much to admire.

Father says Dr. Silliman was born in a tavern in Connecticut, surrounded by spirits. And that's how he ended up a chemist!

Some news from the harbor. Captain Sawgrass is building a ship that has both a tiller and a wheel. He and his shipwright couldn't decide which steering mechanism is better, so they incorporated both. This reminds me of the Elgin cutlass pistols you and your shipmates have on board, half gun, half knife. Capt. Couthouy told us the Navy had them made specifically for the voyage and purchased as many as 150. He calls them a "stupid"

invention, and blames their design for Wilkes Henry's death, and possibly Officer Underwood's as well.

Oh, the questions we have for you, once you return!

Your always loving Cath

SUMMER, 1895

Her encounter with Dickens had a lasting effect on Catharine in a way you might not expect. She began reading every publication she could find—by the Englishwoman Mary Anning, that is, not Dickens. A handful of geologists had been uncovering fossilized remains in the Connecticut Valley since the early 1830s, and the more Cath read about the British paleontologist and her discoveries, the more she sided with those who said the large Valley bones must also signify extinct creatures. After Cath's death, the Boston Society of Natural History added dinosaur footprints to its collection, one of the first museums to do so.[134]

But there's more. Mary Anning advanced the theory that some of her dug-up fossils were giant long-lost birds. Cath saw this as evidence of what the Mr. Cabots of the world refused to accept, that present-day bird populations could spiral into decline and completely die out.

As for the Elgin cutlass pistol, there's a terrible irony about that firearm—now obsolete, thank God. Picture a 16-inch-long pistol with a rigid blade running below the muzzle. Yes, the Navy enlisted George Elgin to design this cumbersome pistol-saber combination for the Wilkes voyage to the Southern Ocean, a weapon that might come in handy if pirates stormed the deck. The idea was to shoot them at close range and finish the job with a slash to the throat. Yet the Elgin pistol was partly to blame for one of the most unfortunate episodes of the entire voyage.

In July 1840, while the fleet was in Fiji waters, a group went ashore to Malolo Island intending to barter gifts for food, when a dispute broke out. The natives were willing to trade two pigs, but for a musket and powder, which the sailors weren't willing to part with. The situation turned ugly, with gunfire erupting on the beach and from the ships offshore. Officer Joseph Underwood was clubbed and died in a crew member's arms. Midshipman Wilkes Henry, using his Elgin to shoot a native, was struck from behind by a native, and fell face down in the water and drowned. He was the only son of Capt. Wilkes' widowed sister.

Wilkes cried inconsolably for days and was a changed man after that. He blamed the island's natives for his nephew's death. No one thought to blame the gun. No one ever thinks to blame the gun. Yet if his nephew hadn't been wielding such a dangerous contraption, he might have lived a long life. The intruders' firearms enraged the natives. Here, too, the natives called the foreigners "cowards" for using them.

Sophie, it happens that The Elgin was the first percussion handgun ever used by the U.S. military. Reverend Forsyth's invention spread to the global population nearly forty years after the minister from Belhelvie got it into his head to invent a mechanism that could more accurately kill a bird before it flew away. Little did he know how many people would be killed by an invention originally intended for birds.

February 1842

Dear Charles,

Most eyes fail to notice, but the continent's skies become emptier every day. The stationmaster expects that by spring, Boston's markets will receive more pigeons than ever before from western territories. Thousands already arrive each month. Soon it will be thousands each week. The quantities brought by rail to New York and Chicago are even greater, for there's an insatiable demand. Father has a theory that the more that railroads extend, telegraph lines too, the more birds are killed and go to market.[135]

Lucinda and I have adopted the anonymous saying I came across in Grandfather's desk for our slogan. We only wish we knew the author.

> *We that never can make it,*
> *Yet dare to unmake it,*
> *Dare take it and break it and throw it away.*[136]

How true of the gifts donated to the Society of Natural History this week. Each one remarkable—and so unmakable, by our hands at least! Five birds from the Himalaya mountains, a fœtal porpoise from Portland, the rattle of a snake from a plantation in Louisiana. Meanwhile, Nature continues to subtract from Nature, as Nature does. The insect specimens are badly infected. So are the mammals, which will be subjected to steam heat. For decontaminating the bird collection, Mr. Rogers plans to bake it.[137]

Spencer Pierce's approach is being closely watched. The naturalist preserved a beaver six months ago with a new fluid patented in France. The corpse has no smell and its features haven't spoiled. Father says that the new method, which has the Academy of Sciences' endorsement, is simpler and more effective than embalming. And it's been injected into birds, without disfigurement.[138]

Your mother shared your letter about the sailor on *Flying Fish*, how he was caught drinking the alcohol used for preserving specimens. The lashings he received must have sobered him up very quickly!

James would like to visit every day but I discourage him. He needs to keep up his work, his interests; and time spent with others. You'll get on well with him and appreciate his head for gadgetry. Wherever he goes, he's sizing things up, figuring new models. It's hard to explain exactly how his mind works, but here's a good example.

The other day we walked down to the wharves. The seas were perfectly calm, and yet large gentle swells were rolling in, maybe from some distant storm, and a boat in the harbor caught his eye, how its rudder rose and fell with the swells. It struck him as similar to the up-down motion of a steam-engine's piston. Now he's keen to harness that motion as a reliable source of power.

It's an inventor's job, he feels, to take risks & move the world forward, or it will stay stuck in one place. He has other big dreams related to the ocean, which you'll hear about once you're back and settled.

March 1842

Dear Cousin,

The smallest sights from my bedroom window bring pleasure. This morning, a robin alighting on the grillwork. The milkman talking to his horse. Marge Williams emerging from her door across the street and taking off at a trot. She always runs from place to place, her hand on her hat to keep it from flying off!

The will to live is strong, but the flesh doesn't obey. If only love alone sustained life!

A Troc'ulus from yesterday's paper feels close and personal. A dockworker spotted a small scorpion in a shipment of sugar from the West Indies. He took it to the customhouse and placed it on a glass for others to look at. It appeared alive but sluggish. But when the glass was placed in the sun, it livened up. Someone watching had heard that if a scorpion finds itself in mortal danger, it will cause its own destruction. This was put to the test. The scorpion was encircled by a piece of cotton dipped in spirits and set ablaze. It tried to escape, but there was no escape possible from the hot flames. It turned up its tail, stung itself in the head, and was dead in an instant.

Wild creatures always have the right instincts. But humans—sometimes I think too much civilization has dulled our best instincts.

Two swans at the Public Garden's conservatory have died suddenly. Mr. Teschemacher is quite sure they ate the leaves of the poisonous oleander that grew on one bank. He blames himself for this oversight, for not having removed the plant sooner. The pair is currently at the Society, and, once they are mounted, they will go on display.[139]

Your mother gamely visited yesterday. It was sleeting and very raw, yet she made the trip from Salem. She looked so lovely, blue eyes glistening and wrapped warmly in the colorful woolen shawl you sent from Peru. Of course we talked about you and the Voyage the entire time. It warms my heart to know you are still due in Boston in June.

April 1842

James brought around a carriage last night & we attended the concert of Frederic Rackemann, the younger brother of Louis. He has just landed from overseas. Fairer and slighter than Louis, he's more delicate in looks. Yet his performance was superior to anything of the kind heard in this city. He outshone even his brother.[140] The rapidity of his fingers. The perfect flow of running passages. It's impossible to adequately convey his genius, except to say that he made the piano sing like a bird.

The rose James gave me is wrapped in tissue and placed with these letters. I'd like to know its entire story, why its petals are so deeply red, the reason for its sweet fragrance and thick, sharp thorns. Those are secrets, I suspect, that no human can ever hope to know. To thoroughly know a rose, you'd have to be one, don't you imagine?

Your loving Cath

SUMMER, 1895

Little Bear, Catharine's last letter contains a list of species that naturalists through the years have named "Pickering"—in honor of Charles. The handwriting changes partway through, leading me to believe that after she died, someone kept updating the list. James Cutting, quite likely.

Calamoagrostis pickeringii, Pickering's reed grass

Stylisma pickeringii, Pickering's dawnflower, a vine

Ivesia pickeringii, or Pickering's ivesia, a type of Rose

Draba pickeringii, Peruvian and Chilean plant composed of many rosettes

Other plants: *Lupinus pickeringii, Oxalis Pickeringii, Saxifraga pickeringii*[141]

Ducula pickeringii, the Grey imperial pigeon

Thamnophis sirtalis pickeringii, the Puget Sound garter snake

Hyla pickeringii, the Pickering tree frog, the spring peeper, the peeping frog

Attached to the clutch of letters, you'll find this small story. I recognize Charles' diminutive script, and suspect this is a Troc'ulus he added to the drawer after James Cutting's death. It has to do with the little frog on the above list.

H. Pickeringii, the Pickering peeper, is the most abundant of the frogs found in several Massachusetts towns. Along with the wood frog, it is the first voice to be heard in spring and the last to become silent in autumn. For so tiny a presence, it is surprisingly loud.

Catharine and I had a memorable encounter with this small amphibian. It was early spring, and during the course of long walk through the countryside, we came to a small shallow pond next to a meadow. The peepers, we noticed, were in a frenzy, swimming about and climbing up on the sides of the pond or onto any available weed stalk. Their enemy, the shad frogs, were swimming below, ready to do them harm.

Suddenly a gust of wind swept a shower of dead leaves down from an oak that had remained on the tree all winter, scattering them across the water. No sooner were these graceful rafts afloat than the peepers appropriated them as points of safety, nearly all of them becoming freighted with a little frog. Hither and thither with the eddying breeze they sailed, while the shad frogs swam under them, the curled and upturned edges of the leaves concealing the Pickeringii from sight.[142]

We sat on the bank and watched these little survivors for nearly an hour.

On June 10th, 1842, the *Vincennes* anchored off Sandy Hook due south of Manhattan Island. No ships were there to greet the returning sailors; no fireworks lit up the shore. But you can be certain that neither the rainy night nor bleak coastline robbed Charles and his shipmates of the joy they felt to be back in familiar waters.

Once in Boston, Charles had a hard time adjusting to the noise of carriages, marketers, and other street sounds. During the day, the sky overhead was obscured by buildings and trees, so different from the open ocean. At night, there were fewer stars and the moon looked small.

When he paid a visit to Tontine Crescent, where he was warmly welcomed by his aunt, uncle and Mary, it was strangely quiet without Catharine present. A forest without leaves stirring. As children, they had been two small animals on the loose, sledding down the Common's long hill or squatting over tidal pools in Salem. As adults, they had been each other's steadfast listener and confidante. Cath would have laughed with delight to hear about the monkey that stole Capt. Wilkes' pipe. Shuddered over Charles' encounter with a giant anaconda. Been transfixed by his descriptions of a white-colored royal blue kingfishers in the mangroves of Fiji.

One night after his return, Charles asked James Cutting to dine with him at the Tremont House. The young man across the table—his racing speech, his serious eye, his odd quips—wasn't what Charles had been expecting. James would mention to me that the man across the table wasn't what he expected! Charles struck him as fussy and fidgety as an old lady. During the meal, he cleaned his glasses every few minutes and kept brushing barely visible crumbs off the tablecloth.

But there they were, with Catharine in common and a deep reverence for Nature. Walking across the Common that evening, Charles to his townhouse on Beacon Street and James to his carriage, they heard a muffled hooting. An owl in the city! "Who-cooks-for-you, who-cooks-for-you-all," James blurted out, mimicking the barred. Charles emitted his rarely heard galumph of a laugh. The two men would never be soul-mates, but right then a friendship clicked into place.

The ocean voyage had changed Charles. He was thinner, grayer and weighed down by detail. He had observed something close to 5,000 species and taken extensive notes on most. The job of formalizing his descriptions remained, and soon he'd be a slave to the tomes that occupied him the rest of his life.

But first, off to Washington he went. A special committee chaired by Joel Poinsett had appointed him curator of the Expedition's thousands of objects stored in the new Patent Office building.[143] Who better for the job! Charles would organize the great jumble in his compulsive, meticulous way. Sophie, the Smithsonian's vast collection should make you proud. It owes so much to our painstaking cousin. His thumbprints are all over its earliest relics.

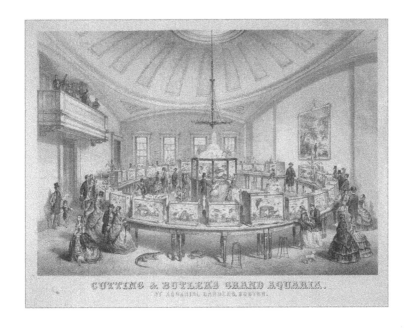

Cutting & Butler's Grand Aquaria, At Aquarial Gardens, Boston

PART II

The Inventor

FALL, 1895

Sophie, you asked me to write down as much as I remember about James and his unfortunate rise and fall. And I will, since I feel the same as you do. Given his achievements, he deserves to be remembered in the same light as other great inventors of his day. Yet the name "James Ambrose Cutting" has disappeared as quickly as a stone tossed overboard. Hardly anyone speaks of him. Hardly anyone recalls that, after his considerable contributions to photography, he went on to create, nearly single-handedly, the world's first public aquarium. Few even realize that an aquarium once existed on a downtown street in Boston known today for its jewelers and watchmakers. Or that a man of his genius was behind it.

The first time I met James was in the summer of 1840, when I was a hoodlum of twelve and he was a rising-star in his mid-twenties. The way he wore his cap just so and carried a magnificent shiny telescope in a satchel across his back put me on best behavior, which wasn't much to speak of—my behavior, that is. Instantly he was my hero, for there was an alluring intensity about him that, even as a boy, I instinctively responded to, a strength of character that sprang from an unusually gifted mind.

Selective memory is a curious thing. About that day, the day that Cath and James, brave souls, took Abigail Warburton, Sarah Apley, and me on a trip to Salem, my only memory of Abigail is that her shoelaces kept coming untied, and we had to keep waiting for her. The vision of Sarah, on the other hand, is complete and indelible. Seventy years have passed, and I can still see the soft blue of her jumper and the wisps of blond hair that stuck to the corners of her mouth as we ran through Broad Field's tall grasses and played hide-and-seek in the old burial ground across from the ancestral home.

Sarah was one reason my mischievousness, edged by an inner disharmony, began to subside that hot August day. Very simply, I began to feel happier. Cath and James were two even bigger reasons. You might say they filled a parental void, for my own parents were nowhere to be found. Emotionally-speaking, that is. They were as ill-suited for one another as a bullfrog and a finch, but since divorce was frowned upon, they lived in separate parts of the house, emerging only for meals and visitors.

I suppose that's why I spent so much of my boyhood putting creepy and slimy things in carefully chosen places—to be noticed, if only to be scolded. A slimy frog in the maid's bed. Pink earthworms dropped from the attic onto top hats passing below. The present of a slug in a pocket.

When my parents handed me over to Catharine for tutoring, I could tell by the alert look in her eye that I wasn't going to get away with much, not even a judiciously placed cockroach. Besides, someone who laughs so easily, who is so kind and unflappable, squelches mischievous thoughts. I believe I instantly fell for her, in a boyish way, feeling the love James felt, but at a more junior level. There are certain people everyone falls in love with, and Cath was that special kind.

Her kindness, which came to her as naturally as breathing, was invincible, almost religious in nature, and turned my mischievousness into confused mush. It must have worked its way into James as well, pulling him in from a distant planet. James had a shock of red hair so thick, his cap sat high on his head. He had serious blue eyes, a long straight nose and a wide level mouth, and it often seemed as though he was terribly distant, dreaming of inventions, except for when Cath was around. I wouldn't appreciate what Cath appreciated until I was much older, which is that James marched to his own drummer, and that the unusual tools he made were an extension of this trait. But when Cath was near, his focus settled.

Men in those days were practically born with the mechanical ability. James' genius went further, for several of his inventions had no antecedents. There was his compact toaster, possibly the first in America to utilize a low gas flame. His fire extinguisher. And of course his famous aerator.

Catharine used to say James had a lot in common with a typical Pickering, and this must have attracted her as well.

Tireless carpenters and farmers fill our family tree; also, naturalists, entrepreneurs, scientists, and politicians known for their energy. Colonel Tim, during his years as Postmaster General, quadrupled the country's post offices, from 89 to 450. But James particularly reminds me of William Pickering, a risk-taker who chose to escape the routine of farming and go to sea. On his way to becoming a successful merchant, William established shipping routes up and down the coast. Colonel Tim relished telling stories about his great uncle. His favorite was the time, during the Queen Anne's War, when William's fishing vessel was attacked by a shallop with some thirty Frenchmen on board. William's six or so crew wanted to surrender. But as each man had a musket, their cool-headed skipper told them to stick to the job of loading their guns and he would take care of firing them. As the enemy rowed within musket-shot range, William ran from port to starboard firing out the cabin portholes and killing or wounding so many of the French, those remaining rowed away as fast as they could.

"And then there was the time," Timothy liked to recount, "that Uncle William had a corn on his toe that was so painful, he went to the joiner's shop and borrowed a chisel and hammer, and didn't he cut off that offending toe and toss it aside like a corn husk!"

William's adventurous nature cost him when he and his ship went down off Nova Scotia during a terrific storm. Eventually, James Cutting also ran into trouble. So it often is with risk-takers.

But back to our trip to Salem on that hot August day.

Our first stop was the ancestral home on Broad Street. I've always found it rather spooky; it's so dark inside, and the floorboards moan like family ghosts. In the library, where the low ceiling is a good measure of the short-ness of our forefathers, there's a certain smell—closer to an odor than a scent—that represents a plausible history of smells of crumbling books, trapped cigar smoke, dried flowers, crumbs in floor cracks and ancient halitosis. Architecturally, the house is a masterful mosaic. If you were to ask it which era it belonged to, it wouldn't know quite how to respond. The first John Pickering, the carpenter from England, built a small saltbox with white oak cut from a nearby swamp. Future generations kept adding to it, applying whatever architectural style was in vogue at the time, and it became a mansion. In the 1830s, the John who was then owner, Gothic-struck, added roof peaks, gables, and a fence with obelisk finials.

"Salem's oldest house, America's oldest home," historians claim, in light of how many generations of Pickerings have lived there.

In the afternoon our small group crossed Broad Field and followed the path down to the brook to hunt fish. Cath and James occasionally looped fingers. They were good friends, I gathered. A dusky brown bird landed in an apple tree on one side of the path and started singing. I reached for my peashooter, but Cath had her eye on me.

"Oliver!"

We stood quietly as the small whisk of feathers sang emphatically.

"Imagine you're a bird, Ollie," said James. "You've made it through the gungies of winter, and now summer's sun is warming your feathers, and you and all the other woodland creatures feel a sun-inspired sassypurriness that raises songs of joy from every little bird mouth around, a glad chorus that fizzilates and tippilates throughout the forest!"

Abigail, Sarah and I didn't know what to think of this odd man Cath had brought along. He sounded like no other adult we had ever met. We con-tinued on to the brook where we caught herring in our nets and sailed bark boats. Later, weaving our way back through Broad Field, we chased rabbits, poked our fingers down vole holes, and hid and hopped in the long grasses. To pass the time on the carriage ride to the city, the three of us started speaking gobbledygook, then sang silly rhymes until, giggled out, we dissolved into a heap on the carriage floor.

Heaven knows how Cath and James stood us that day.

Never again did I aim my peashooter at a bird or any creature. Not that I consciously made an oath not to. It just wasn't a fun game to play anymore. I'm pretty sure, too, that my young brain sopped up James as a no-hunt, no-shoot model worth emulating.

I don't remember seeing James at Catharine's service two years later. He was somewhere in that large somber crowd, just as he must have been at the services for Uncle John and Aunt Sarah six years later. Losing those three made it feel as though an extinction had occurred.

Several years passed. Then one afternoon, while I was doing some research at Boston's Society of Natural History, quite out of the blue James dropped off two specimens, a large boa constrictor and two pipe fishes.[144] Once again the Society had moved to larger quarters, this time to Mason Street, a few blocks from its former address. He clasped me tight. How was I? Where was I living? How did I like working for Smyth, the civil engineer? He and Mary kept in close touch, and Mary must have told him about my employer.

In my early twenties by then, I noticed things about James I hadn't in my youth. He was shorter than I recalled and had an unflinching gaze. When he picked up the book I was reading—*The Water Supply of the City of Rome*, Frontinus's classic —and stared hard at it, I was also struck by his hands. Capable hands, muscular and taut. They didn't look comfortable in a resting position. Which James wasn't in general. Awkward when seated, he seemed far more comfortable standing at his workbench or striding through the woods, watchful and active.

I caught him up as best I could. He listened, but I could tell he was afloat in the past. I reminded him of Cath, and my sheer presence brought her back. We might have been at a séance, and I was but the mediator.

For a long time after Catharine's death, James had shut himself away to such an extent that sometimes Mary sent him a message. "Are you alive? If so, join us for dinner!" Despite his heavy heart, he crafted some remarkable innovations during this period. One of them, a new style of gas lamp, ended up in several establishments throughout the city. The Boston Museum acquired it, and now that it was splendidly illuminated, the Museum could be visited late into the evening.[145] Another of his designs, a fire extinguisher, replaced water with a flame retardant.

Looking at me with serious eyes, he spoke in a rapid burst. This odd mannerism I very much remembered. "Smyth-rounddown-gutta-percha-South-East-Asia-globalcommun-cable." He paused and asked, "Are you helping with that?"

Not many people outside of the engineering field knew of my employer, William Smyth, or of his recent contribution, although, if James subscribed to *Boston Mechanic*, he would have read about the unusual undertaking. Engineers on both sides of the Atlantic were experimenting with laying cable across the seafloor for telegraphic communications—a consequence of Mr. Morse's invention—and Smyth had recommended they use a resin from the Pertja tree in South East Asia for insulating the cable and protecting it from water pressure and marine life. Smyth had seen natives in Malaysia coat the bottom of their boats with the rubbery substance and make everything from knife handles to necklaces with it.

I was on the fringes of that project. But I had handled gutta-percha, a most amazing substance. As the sap dried, you could roll it into a ball that ended up hard but bouncy. The British were onto something, making golf balls out of it.[146]

James took a seat opposite me. He was full of questions about the ocean cable.

"The wires are embedded in the gutta-percha?"

Yes, and Smyth was thinking it might be a good idea to coil hempen rope round the gutta-percha for further protection.

"How strong is gutta-percha?"

Strong, very strong. However.... I hesitated, uncertain whether Smyth would like me sharing this. But with James' eye pinned on me, it was impossible not to continue.

However, engineers with the British Indian Telegraph Company had run into a problem. The cable they were testing off Singapore worked well for a while and then suddenly stopped working.[147] A ship went out to investigate, and in thirty fathoms of water divers found a deep gouge in the cable, a cut that had severed three of the cable's seven wires. A bony substance was pulled from the gouge. At first it was thought to be a shark's tooth. But an ichthyologist was consulted who felt that a shark would leave bite marks on both sides of the cable. The ichthyologist put the bony substance on his mantelpiece at home and continued to occasionally inspect it, until, one day, the answer popped into his head. The gouge must be the work of a sawfish, a species he once had caught off the Andaman Islands. He requested a sawfish's tooth from the British museum and hammered it into a piece of cable that the engineers gave him. Sure enough, the damage resembled the original gash! While foraging along the seafloor, a large sawfish must have sunk his teeth into the cable, and when he furiously tried to withdraw, a tooth broke off.

"Astonishing!" James was literally on the edge of his chair.

He wanted to know more, so on I jabbered. The engineers who were donning underwater helmets in order to plunge to the ocean bottom and lay cables were encountering exotic creatures never seen before. Apparently, the old thinking that the seafloor was as desolate as the moon was dead wrong.

"Really! What sort of creatures?"

Sea anemones, worms and urchins, unusual mollusks and all sorts of fish there were no names for. I wanted to sound like I knew what I was talking about, but I really didn't, not being directly involved with the project.

James stayed for about an hour, asking more questions and sharing his own thoughts about the curious dwellers of Neptune's paradise. Before he left, he made me promise to pay a visit to his studio downtown.

By then, his lamps and his parlor beehive, admired both as a novelty and a handsome piece of furniture, had made him another small fortune.[148] He had changed course yet again, and was now bearing down on photography, a technology he'd been interested in since before the camera obscura's invention. Boston was full of semi-competent photographers who were cashing in on the public's craze to be photographed. James, by comparison, was a self-taught authority. Hiring several assistants—a man to polish and coat the plates, another to develop the plates, and an artist for tinting the image—he had opened Cutting's Portrait Studio and, within a month's time, customers were lined up at the door.

I did visit his studio—we stayed in close touch from then on—and portraits, I found out, were only his day job. After he hung the "Closed" sign on the door each evening, he went into the back room and got busy with chemicals and glassware. He was still trying to improve upon the flawed daguerreotype. His solitary work often carried on until the moon was descending. For the sake of convenience, he had sold his property beside Swallow Pond and now lived steps away from his studio, on the cusp of the harbor.

Burning the midnight oil paid off. In 1855 he patented his method. He named the new type of image an "ambrotype," after his middle name "Ambrose," and for a while ambrotypes captured the market. Made on glass, they cost less than daguerreotypes on silver-plated copper and could be taken in one-quarter the time. James' trade secret of using Canadian balsam to seal the image resulted in a greater softness and finish.[149]

Newspapers in several cities ran advertisements: "Ambrotypes! These pictures-on-glass, immensely superior over the old style in tone, clearness, and beauty, are becoming exceedingly and deservedly popular. They are the result of a new and exquisite process lately discovered and patented by James A. Cutting of Boston."[150]

But as often happens, it wasn't long before a different process stole the show, the tintype. Tintypes were cheaper still and less fragile.[151] In time, these pictures-on-metal framed Billy the Kid holding his Winchester rifle and Civil War soldiers shouldering their muskets—some of which, you should take note, were old flint-locks retrofitted with the percussion mechanism.[152]

Yes, Reverend Forsyth's technology for a more accurate killing of birds had come to the battlefield. It was a devastating development that was scarcely commented upon.

Leaps in technology were to be expected. James wasn't too terribly upset that his process had been superseded. He had made a tidy sum from the rights for the ambrotype and used some of the money to purchase a smart-looking, seaworthy yacht, which he appropriately named *Ambrotype*. Hiring a captain and crew, he took friends on cruises as far north as the St. Lawrence or south beyond Long Island Sound. You asked what occurred to make him switch so quickly from photography to ocean science. Pleasure trips on *Ambrotype* had lots to do with it. Creatures of the "briny deep" always had fascinated him, and now he had time to cruise anywhere he pleased, drop nets and fishline overboard, and launch his own investigations.

I once went along for a day's fishing junket. Dr. Storer was on board, and he and James huddled together next to the rail discussing every rock cod, haddock, hake, and sculpin pulled over the side. His vessel, I realized, had become James' workbench, the ocean his laboratory.

He surprised us with some news that day. He was opening a public aquarium in Boston in the spring, and he even had a partner willing to bankroll the enterprise, Henry Butler, a wealthy New Yorker.

Mr. Butler, who had written a popular book on family fish tanks, was also part-owner of Phineas Barnum's American Museum in New York. Barnum's business had gone bankrupt, just like the time before, and he had sold the museum to Henry Butler and John Greenwood, with the agreement that he would stay on as an employee. The new owners intended to continue his philosophy of attracting the public with the *outlandish*, the *highly curious*. The Feejee Mermaid remained in residence and still drew audiences, while a new exhibit, the six-foot-tall "Man-Eating Chicken," was possibly Barnum's most preposterous ruse ever, and also a star attraction. Heavens knows why, because all the ticketholder got for his money was a tall man eating fried chicken.

As for James' new venture, it seemed a good bet that with Mr. Butler and his money behind it, and James at its helm, the new aquarium would be wildly successful. Nothing less than the aquarium at London's Regent's Park.[153] James had the ingenuity and integrity to make it so.

James on his own, and Henry Butler as well, had been developing fish tanks since the mid-1850s.[154] A new trend in family parlors was to supplant fish globes, which needed the water changed, with aquariums, which didn't. Reciprocity between plants and fish was the secret. The water in an aquarium didn't need changing because plants threw off oxygen, an important staple for fish, while fish threw off carbonic acid, a necessary ingredient for plant growth.

However, James was studying how to do this on a much larger scale, for public display.

I remember thinking his enterprise was bound to flourish for another reason. P.T. Barnum wasn't involved!

Right on schedule, Boston Aquarial Gardens opened the following April in a large upper-floor space on Bromfield Street formerly occupied by the Mercantile Library Association, where light flooded in through a large center dome and high side windows.[155] The aquarium took Boston completely by surprise. People were amazed that fish could be exhibited like animals in a zoo and live outside their wild environment. They couldn't get enough of what they saw and watched the pools and tanks for hours on end. Praise for "Mr. Cutting's Aquarial Gardens" poured in from all quarters. One of the new aquarium's keenest enthusiasts was Louis Agassiz, the Swiss naturalist. Agassiz was ensconced as a professor of natural history at Harvard by then, and the college was so delighted to have the fish expert on its faculty, it was constructing a natural history museum for Agassiz to direct and curate.

Here was another man of infinite energy and interests. In fact, Agassiz always had so many balls in the air that he was apt to lose track of a few. "Like a splendid butterfly, he flew from one delight to another," a friend of his remarked.

Aquarial Gardens, the moment its doors swung open, became one of Agassiz's foremost delights, and despite his own museum-in-the-making, which opened a year later, and despite his students and a long list of other commitments, Agassiz accepted James' proposal and became a consultant for the new aquarium. He was arguably Boston's most famous scientist at the time, certainly its best-connected—many of the old scientific guard in Europe were his close friends—so it was a feather in James' cap to have this European superstar promoting the aquarium wherever he went.

"Oh, to be sure, Paris, London, Dublin, and Hamburg have great aquariums, but each is part of a museum complex that has other exhibits," Agassiz told his colleagues, students and Saturday Club dinner mates. "Mr. Cutting's is the only public aquarium dedicated solely to marine life—in the vorld!—and this is tremendously valuable. You valk up its steep staircase, you enter under the sea, and you never depart the sea until you valk back down the steps!

"And vhile you're there, it's as if you svim among hundreds and hundreds of vishies!"

The press swooned; the public swooned. Boston was overjoyed to have this fish palace in its midst and proud that the world's most famous ichthyologist visited Bromfield Street on a regular basis. Agassiz solidified Aquarial Gardens' reputation.

(Just to make note: When Agassiz first moved to Cambridge, our cousin Charles persuaded him to take on the herculean job of writing up the U.S. Exploring Expedition's report on fish species. The professor labored for years on the manuscript, which grew to over two-thousand pages. Unfortunately, the Civil War interrupted its publication, and when Agassiz died a decade later, it still wasn't published. Worse still, no one could find it.)

As different as Agassiz and James were—one flamboyant, brilliant, and messy; the other reserved, brilliant, and methodical—they got on famously, united by a mutual interest in fish as well as a disliking of technologies that threatened Nature's creatures, notably guns.

James found out about his new friend's attitude toward guns in the summer of 1858, when James joined Agassiz and other members of The Saturday Club on a camping trip. The regulars shared a love of literature, good conversation and fine wine, and even though James wasn't a regular, his creative mind made him a welcome addition. They canoed and portaged their way into the dense interior of the Adirondacks, where they threw up a shelter beside Follansbee Pond. The party included Amos Binney, James Russell Lowell, Ralph Waldo Emerson, Jeffries Wyman, and a few others.[156] Longfellow, who often went on these outings, had no desire to this time—because Emerson was bringing his gun! The philosopher could be so absentminded, his head buried in the Ancients, the poet feared an accident.

"Someone will get shot!" he fretted.

(Within that memorable group was Jeffries Wyman, an anatomist who presided over the American Assoc. of Science. Wyman had played a key role in identifying the bones in John Webster's furnace as those of Dr. Parkman. And it was Wyman who, at a meeting at the Boston Society of Natural History in 1847, was the first to fully describe a beast from Africa, which was neither human nor chimpanzee. He named it a "gorilla," after a former tribe of wild Africans. When they were together, Agassiz and Wyman often bickered. Wyman, on one hand, felt the evidence was irrefutable; anatomical differences between Negroes and Caucasians were insignificant, whereas major differences occurred between Negroes and apes. Agassiz vehemently disagreed, arguing the black and white races were significantly different, and thus had been created separately.)

After breakfast one morning, a few of the men took up target practice. They asked Agassiz to join them, but he refused. The professor, along with Dr. Wyman and James, was busy studying the stomach of a gunned down deer, which Dr. Wyman wanted to remove and dry out; it would make a good specimen for his students. The others kept pestering Agassiz. "Ah! a brilliant scientist must be an excellent shot!" He finally gave in, took up a rifle and hit the mark dead center. There was a burst of applause. Again! Again! No, he replied, he'd quit while he was ahead. When they badgered him some more, he turned his back on them.

"I sense you don't think much of guns," said James.

"You sense right," Agassiz confessed. "Guns are for savages, not civilized types!" This was his first time pulling a trigger in ages, and his bull's-eye was sheer luck, he claimed.

"I don't agree with Mr. Darwin's theories. But guns! I agree with him about guns. On *Beagle*, Darwin gave in to his shooting craze and brought down just about anything that moved. But he began to realize, shooting vas getting in the vay of observing, and he put his gun avay. It was far more peaceful to *look* than to *kill*. He saw twice as much, learned twice as much."[157]

It's easy to see why Agassiz and James got on famously after that.

Boston Aquarial Gardens began with only a few tanks. The rush on tickets, however, allowed James to expand the floor plan, until forty smaller pools surrounded a large center pool that held two languid sturgeons.

"Come gaze upon *Life beneath the waters*," one advertisement read. "Come gaze upon water-soldiers and hermit-crabs, sea-cucumbers and starfish; upon families of perch and a pair of tremendous sturgeon; upon the marvelous sight of a stickleback building his nest like a bird, imported corals, rudder fish, long-nosed pickerel, and a fish lizard transported from Lake Superior!"[158]

In June, my employer Smyth fell ill. Placed on temporary leave, I finally climbed the steep staircase on Bromfield Street one afternoon, entered through a heavy door, and found myself in another world. "Cutting's Aquarium," as reporters and the public referred to it, was as impressive as I knew it would be. It was James—the mastermind, the impresario, the inventor—at the top of his game. He had authentically reenacted the habitats of both underwater worlds, fresh and salt, and filled them with dazzling denizens that swam or scuttled, drifted or sat or attached. There were larger fish like black bass, rudder fish, and long-nosed pickerel, and an immense number of smaller types, like minnow, barnacle, and water newt.

I didn't return to my Beacon Hill apartment until after ten that evening. The lateness of the hour might have been because I had lost myself in fish watching, as visitors to the aquarium were apt to do. Yet something else kept me downtown.

After touring the aquarium, I'd gone with James next door to the Wild Horse Tavern, where, over rabbit stew and several pints, he unexpectedly bared his soul.

"The tanks need to be refigured. Completely refigured!" he kept repeating. A major problem had arisen, and his despair was troubling to see. Would I give him a hand until Smyth recovered and needed me back? He'd pay good wages.

Aquarial Gardens was proving so irresistible, it was on its way to outshining the Boston Museum as Boston's most popular destination. I said yes to his offer, but not because of the aquarium's rising reputation, or because its operations fascinated me, but because my boyhood champion was so distraught. To turn him down—well, it never crossed my mind. Moreover, my work for Smyth dealt with urban waterways and provided some familiarity with the mechanisms that needed fixing at the aquarium.

The obstacles James had overcome to simply open the aquarium!—had they been barriers in a jumping competition, they would have been twice as high as the horse. Figuring out the right specifications for the plate glass and finding the right artisan. Capturing the various fish and knowing what to feed them. Transplanting aquatic plants and keeping them alive. James had felt his way along, working largely from scratch. One by one the obstacles gave way.

But then this alarming problem arose. Aquatic plants in the tanks that released oxygen to sustain the fish were decomposing faster than James expected them to, and as the weeks passed, the detritus clouded the water so much, the fish were barely visible. Worse, the water was turning noxious and unhealthy. He added snails to the tanks to eat up the detritus. But they were slow workers, and the situation only marginally improved.

So he decided to switch to an invention of his own design, his aerator. A cruder device was in use at the Dublin Zoological Gardens, and James had made the long ocean crossing just to study it with his own eyes. A large pair of bellows rested on a platform, and attached to its nozzle were tubes made of gutta-percha that connected to the fish tanks. An attendant had the job of squeezing the bellows, which oxygenated the water in the tanks without relying solely on the plants. The attendant didn't have much to do, because visitors took to working the bellows, liking the sight of bubbles streaming upwards and knowing they were helping the fish.

James' invention was light-years beyond this primitive setup. He managed to anticipate the local workings of electricity, which, remember, wasn't captured for everyday use until later in the century. In each fish tank, a descending weight pushed down on a reservoir of air, forcing the air through rubber tubing into the tank. The weights were calibrated to descend so slowly; they only had to be reset once a day. It was similar to rewinding a watch every twenty-four hours.

The changeover took us three exhausting days. We emptied the tanks, cleaned them, set an aerator in each one, and re-filled them. When the aquarium reopened, visitors were mostly absorbed by the sight of the fish, and only a few noticed the new apparatus. But the water was so translucent, everyone noticed how the fish sparkled.

"The introduction of air, by a process of Mr. Cutting's own invention, renders the tanks more clear and beautiful than ever," the Boston Daily Advertiser raved. "Cutting's aerator" received a patent in 1861. The bubbles rising up in the corners of the tanks intrigued people, but few grasped the enormity of James' breakthrough. The modern aquarium was born.[159]

Aquatic plants would still adorn tanks for habitat enhancement and aesthetics, but they were no longer a necessity. "Cutting's aerator" and later versions would be, for the health and longevity of the fish.

Once that problem was fixed, and the fish seemed reasonably happy, James was fairly confident that the basic principles upholding his ocean palace could support larger creatures. Why not put a yellowfin on display? Why not a blue shark? As he added larger species, he learned their needs as he went along, becoming more confident that bigger denizens-of-the-deep could be kept alive on Bromfield Street.

In July, two young seals caught in Maine were transported by wagon to Bromfield Street, where they lived in and out of a large saltwater pool. James named them "Ned" and "Fanny," and, discerning that they were exceptionally intelligent, as well as curious and playful, he set about turning them into performers. His style was to be patient and kind, never impertinent or scolding. One of my jobs that summer was helping to feed the aquarium's stable, and I often was poolside when James was training the pair and admired his firm but gentle manner. It was astonishing how fast the seals learned. He only had to lead them through a trick once or twice, and they were ready for an audience.

Before summer was over, the "learned seals" were The Garden's top attraction. Fanny, who was capable of a range of skits, particularly beguiled audiences with her "good-night" routine. She'd lie on her back, fold her flippers on her breast, then fall asleep and start snoring. The louder she snored, the louder the audience laughed. James and I agreed that Fanny understood how comical she was—she loved the attention. Ned's act of waking in the morning and grooming himself for the day was equally entertaining. Another crowd pleaser was when he cranked a hand organ with one flipper and blew kisses to ladies in the audience with the other.

The watchman got quite a fright one night when the organ suddenly started up. It was Ned, with not a lot else to do. His nocturnal playing became routine. Apparently, he liked the organ's sound, which surprised us at first. But why shouldn't animals derive pleasure from the sound of music the same as humans do?

Sometimes I arrived with a pail of fresh mackerel, and the seal pair would be splashing toward me, when James' arrival made them hurry to him instead. They radiated pure joy in his presence, their expressions bright, their manner frisky. Many were the times James sat idly beside them, chatting with them while brushing their fur with a currycomb—which Agassiz said kept down parasites—their large round eyes never leaving his face, his eyes never leaving theirs. If he stopped, their noses nudged his arm and he continued. I'm quite sure James loved the seals more than he did most people. He understood mammals, fish and birds better than anyone I've ever known, and they sensed this and trusted him implicitly.

For over a year, all aspects of the aquarium kept improving. James' attention to detail was why. In essence, he was a tireless and patient parent. Many in his family knew him, like the black porgy who came to the surface whenever James whistled. Or the grouper who followed him whenever he walked by its tank. I'm certain all the fish knew him. They were aware of each other, so why wouldn't they recognize this upright creature who tirelessly watched over them.

Visitor hours were from 9 a.m. to 10 p.m., six days a week. James practically lived on the premises, and often spent the night on a cot in his office. When a death occurred, which happened with some frequency, he took it personally.

"What did I do wrong?" he asked Professor Agassiz, when the grey shark died not long after its capture off Portland. "Water quality? Food? Parasites?"

The professor gave him a long look. "My dear James, you are selflessly noble and try so hard to match all the ingredients of the natural ocean for the vishies. The problem is, you never can, you never vill."

The two men were in perfect harmony. They wanted Aquarial Gardens to educate visitors, but with a sprinkle of entertainment. It was Agassiz's idea to place microscopes on a long table so that visitors could inspect a drop of fish blood or a slice of frog intestine. The musicians were James' idea. On Saturday afternoons at teatime, they played on the balcony overlooking the large hall and filled the aquarium with sounds pleasing to both people and fish. It all paid off, every bit of it. Strings of carriages lined up daily, depositing the young and the old. They sometimes lingered in the large room—lit by natural light during the day and gas chandeliers at night—until late in the evening, mesmerized by parading fish and theatrical seals.

When I came to work each day, two fish fossils above the ticket booth always reminded me of Catharine. They were gifts from Professor Agassiz, who had named each species in honor of Mary Anning. *Acrodus anningiae* and *Belenostomus anningiae*. Mary Anning, so admired by Catharine—as well as Charles Dickens. Mary Anning, so convinced that the big-boned monsters she unearthed along England's southern coast were proof of extinction!

Cuvier, Agassiz's former teacher, had proposed the theory of extinction, but it was such a new concept, people weren't sure how it fit with God, creator of all life forms. Agassiz, like Cuvier, accepted that animals could be knocked down by a natural disaster. That they could go extinct. But he was of the belief that because God had created each one, their special types were never-changing. Darwin's idea that one species could transform into another species was nothing sort of blasphemous, in Agassiz's opinion. Darwin had gone too far, British and European naturalists tended to think, while American naturalists were receptive to Darwin's theory.

On his visits to Aquarial Gardens, Agassiz often brought a pod of students—so they might "catch nature in the act," as he put it. Once, when I was passing through the main hall, a student asked such a good question, I stopped to hear the professor's response.

"How can you be sure Mr. Darwin's natural selection *isn't* taking place?" What a stupendously brave student for asking this!

Agassiz replied with his usual rock-solid confidence.

"Easy! So many vossils I've vound, but I've never found vossil evidence to support Darwin's claim that worms evolve into fish, for example. I've never found an intermediary, never a vorm-fish. My colleague Richard Owen in London has unearthed huge extinct animals he calls 'dinosaurs.'" Some people say these creatures became birds, but Richard hasn't vound a shred of evidence. Birds? Ha! The last time I visited Richard, his dog vas chasing flies, trying to eat them. We vondered, was his dog in the act of becoming an insect!"[160]

His laughter boomed through the Aquarium. All the fish must have heard it!

I thought the world of Professor Agassiz. He was magnificently generous in his support of James and the aquarium. But his friends knew that when he formed an opinion, he stuck to it like a barnacle stuck to kelp. It was just like him to say creatures never evolved. His own thinking never evolved!

All the new thinking about evolution, about extinction, about species and their place in the world lured all the more people to Aquarial Gardens. Around this time, Darwin proposed another theory that further shone a spotlight on aquariums. Life may have started in "a warm little pond," he proposed.

With James at the helm, and Agassiz by his side, Aquarial Gardens should have soared into the future. But toward the spring of 1860, there was an unfortunate change. Henry Butler—Butterball Butler, we'd taken to calling him for reasons you can guess—sold his share of the American Museum, or some of it, back to Phineas Barnum, who once again had miraculously risen from the ashes of financial ruin. This meant that Butler was now in Boston more than he was New York. Had he and James seen eye-to-eye, two heads might have been better than one. But Butler's association with Barnum seems to have altered his curatorial tastes, for one cheerless winter's day he broke the news to the staff that The Gardens was in need of more variety. Hence its exhibits and performances would widen beyond aquaria to include jungle animals, actors and musicians.

A larger building was required. A move was imminent.[161]

James was visibly shell-shocked. But what could he do? Even though he was a co-owner, Butler held the purse strings and called the shots. James had to either comply or walk away from everything he had built from the ground up and cared heart-and-soul about, which he wasn't about to do.

The new establishment on Washington Street opened on October 5th, 1860. A banner above the door proclaimed its new name: "The Boston Aquarial & Zoological Gardens." Hundreds attended a lavish opening gala, everyone from notable literati to sea captains to politicians and farmers. The Prince of Wales, who happened to be in town on business, said a few words no one could hear, after which a group of South African Aborigines dressed in native costume sang, danced and pounded on drums. Then Professor Agassiz, a bear of a man, took the stage and gave a short speech everyone could hear.

The new Aquarial & Zoological Gardens was just one instance that year of a groundswell of interest in natural phenomena. In November, Harvard opened its Museum of Comparative Zoology. "Agassiz's Museum," most called it. Agassiz's connections in Europe were such that the museum had received nearly 90,000 specimens, or 11,000 species for display and research. That was more than all the species counted by Linnaeus fifty years earlier![162]

Some of those acquisitions were alive and kept at home by Agassiz. Cousin Charles' favorite story about Agassiz was how, one morning, the professor's wife Elizabeth shouted down to her husband, "Louis, Louis! There's a snake in my shoe," to which Agassiz hollered back, "Leezie, Leezie, Oh no! Where are the other five?"

The Boston Society of Natural History meanwhile was preparing for yet another move, its fourth. This time its directors had decided to construct a building on Berkeley Street in the newest, most elegant part of town, on land that filled the former smelly Bay. The Renaissance-styled brick building would open in 1863, right at the height of the Civil War. What a sign of the times! A throbbing interest in Nature managed to prevail over the bankruptcy of combat.

At the new Aquarial Gardens' opening, Agassiz ended his speech sounding very much like himself. "Every creature under this new roof is an original thought of God, a superb manifestation of our divine maker. Amen." Flame-swallowers and jugglers came on stage, and then a lion-tamer, who cracked his whip on the heels of three gangly lions who leapt onto a wooden pyramid and sat looking moodily over our heads.

James and Agassiz stood moodily at the back of the hall, arms crossed and unsmiling. The scene was too Barnumesque for them. But now that Butterball Butler had "manager" pinned to his lapel, their hands were tied. I knew James was crying on the inside. The marine life in the great upper hall remained in his charge, and we made sure that the airy space was well lit and cheerful, the sixty-five ponds and their occupants carefully cared for. But the injustices happening downstairs! It was a hellhole down there. A windowless performance center stood at one end. The zoo with its sad looking animals occupied the other end. A mangy moose from Maine was caged next to a pair of thin kangaroos from Mongolia. Two Floridian crocodiles that never moved were housed between a ringtail iguana from the Bahamas and a Maine bear and her cubs. On and on the sad scene went, for some forty cages.

The stench downstairs was so unbearable that the doors to the alleyway were left open even on the coldest winter days. There always seemed to be a problem. Infections; deaths; animals wailing; bitten workmen. One day the inhabitants of the deer pen got loose and fled out the exit doors. Upstairs, we celebrated! Hurry, you magnificent beasts. Hurry away from here! The deer were from the Philippines, and even if they had found their way into the country, it's hard to imagine they survived the winter.

The performers who came and went that fall mirrored Butler's crooked ideology. Really, Barnum's. They were entertainingly strange, and their purpose was to build curiosity and sell tickets, period. Mademoiselle Victoria, and her Wondrous Feats of Magic. Madam Lanista, the animal trainer who wrestled with large snakes. Chief Atsaakata and his half-naked Red Men of the Forest. It was alarming to hear that Barnum, stationed in New York, was helping Butler to sign on some of these performers, but not surprising.

James had enough to occupy him that he didn't dwell on the shift from a gallery of serious science to a brothel of cheap amusements, the flash-in-the-pan distractions that he and Agassiz, both educators at heart, spurned. His latest challenge, I suppose, distracted him. He was intent on a system for hauling harbor water from the foot of Summer Street to Washington Street and had persuaded the Directors to spend $10,000 on the conduit. It was a distance of three-quarters of a mile. Conveying saltwater that far had never been attempted, at least not in New England. But James wasn't concerned. Piping freshwater into the city from outlying ponds had been done for several years. If the aquarium was to add larger marine creatures to its assortment, its pools would require fresh seawater on a daily basis.

I was present when James sketched out his plan to the Directors, and he was very convincing. "Here's the route the pipes will take," he said, drawing on a chalkboard. "We'll set them in cement and bury them six feet down. The hardest part will be digging the trenches. At the harbor terminus, we'll rig up a steam engine for pumping the water out of the harbor and sending it on its way. At the Washington Street terminus, another engine will force the water up to a reservoir on the roof, and gravity will do the rest—replenish the tanks below as needed."[163]

Not even Smyth, my employer, who oversaw several freshwater routes into the city, made the passage of 800,000 gallons a day sound like such a trifling matter.

James was right of course. Burying the pipes was the hardest part, and it fell to me to make sure they were put down to specifications, a skill learned from Smyth. It also was my job to reassure merchants that the work would be over soon, the street repaired and passable again. Here, I was out of my depth. One bank owner claimed the trench came closer to his door than he'd been led to believe and threatened a lawsuit. James came to the site and instantly appeased him by giving him, his wife and four children a lifetime pass to The Gardens.

At a meeting in January, the Directors asked James what larger sea animals he had in mind for the aquarium.

"Oh, maybe a walrus. Perhaps a dolphin. And why not a whale!"

At the mention of a whale, the room went silent. After the Directors studied James' face, and saw he was serious, a heated discussion broke out. Some directors were terrifically in favor. Ingenious! Great for business! Others shook their heads and hooted. Absurd! A whale of a silly idea! Completely farfetched!

James tried to reassure them. To catch and transport a living whale, to exhibit it, feed it and keep it healthy were plausible goals if you knew what you were doing. He said this in a perfectly matter-of-fact way.

Henry Butler didn't know what to think. His book on family aquariums began with the statement, "The Leviathan may not be caught, or, in all human probability, his skeleton would now be on exhibition at Barnum's Museum."[164] And now James Cutting was claiming the opposite!

A few days later, this rhyme turned up on the chalkboard in the front office:

James baited his hook with a dragon's tail,
And sat upon a rock and bobbed for whale,
And bobbed and bobbed and bobbed to no avail,
Although he did catch a snail! and then a pail!

But James wasn't to be dissuaded. He knew for sure a whale could be caught, and he knew how to do it. Cruises on *Ambrotype* to the Gulf of St. Lawrence had planted the idea, for it's there that he frequently spied whales. Large pods of them. They were white whales, and they were feeding on an abundance of small fish called capelin, which were feeding on a surplus of plankton. A resourceful Canadian had built weirs for trapping the whales, specifically for their oil and skins. Charles Tetu was his name, and he had invented a useful process for manufacturing leather from the skins of both whales and porpoises.[165]

Toward spring of 1861, James travelled to Canada to make his request in person. Would Mr. Tetu be willing to capture a whale for Boston's Aquarial Gardens?[166] The Canadian was happy to oblige, and at the same time amused by the prospect of taking a whale all the way to Boston. What was James' plan? Push the whale by barge? Pull him by balloon? Hypnotize the leviathan and instruct him to swim south?

Back in Boston, James won over a majority of the Directors, including Butler, who appreciated that a whale in captivity might double ticket sales. He then sent a telegram to Mr. Tetu: "At your next opportunity, please attend to the business we discussed."

Less than a week later, Mr. Tetu telegraphed back: "Your whale is in our weirs!"

The events that followed were wild and exhausting. James and I immediately packed our bags and, accompanied by ten volunteers, journeyed north. Joined by several Canadians, we went to work chopping down trees and squaring wide boards, and quickly built a large wooden tank. The next day we partially filled it with seaweed, leaned it on its side, and, with the help of a dozen more Canadians and several sturdy logs, we rolled the thrashing 16-foot, 1200-pound whale into the tank.[167] Its tail gave several fellows a sound thwack, but no serious injuries resulted. After more seaweed was added to the tank, and the whale was drenched with seawater, a derrick hoisted the box onto a truck that carried it to a rail station twelve miles away. The box was transferred to a railcar pulled by a special engine, and from there the whale's journey continued to Quebec, where, after another transfer, it rode the Grand Trunk Railroad south to Portland.

Each of us took turns "basting" the whale, standing beside him and pouring seawater over his blow-hole with a dipper. I tried to avoid looking into the creature's eye, which was cloudy, unmoving and unreadable. I tried not to think about the incongruity of an ocean creature clickety-clacking over metal tracks. I tried not to think about our cruel abduction of this beautiful animal. But of course I did, and I don't think I slept a wink the entire trip. The farmer who stopped digging to wave at the train, the attendants in the small stations we sped through—they couldn't have guessed in a million years what we had on board.

At Portland, the box was swung onto a Boston-bound steamer. For the rest of its journey, the whale at least had the waves beneath him—but what good was that when he was entombed above them? I'd never felt so guilty about anything in my whole life. To this day I wake up and get a clammy feeling when I think of what we put that whale through.

At the Aquarium there was a near catastrophe. When the wooden box was hoisted over the great crystal pond made for the whale and tipped on its side to release its occupant, the box broke apart with a loud splintering, freeing the whale, whose falling body narrowly missed striking the tank's rim and fell into the water with a great splash that soaked the crowd that had gathered to welcome the whale. Some arrival! The pool was quickly replenished with seawater from the roof.

Everyone said what splendid condition the whale had arrived in. He looked alright on the outside, but on the inside? Who could test the creature's vitals or read his mind and appreciate his emotions. No one outshone James in this regard. But I worried that in his attempt to make the Aquarium the best around, he was losing sight of his own golden rule, which was to treat other animals as you would treat your best friends.

Of course, Boston was ecstatic to discover there was now a white whale residing on Washington Street. The aquarium stayed open an extra hour on summer evenings to accommodate the crush of visitors. James expected to hear from skeptics, and he did, their letters airing in the daily press. That was no whale! someone wrote. It was too small and instead was an albino porpoise! Another writer identified it as a white shark.

Our good emissary Professor Agassiz sent a letter to the *Boston Journal*, setting the record straight.

"I congratulate Mr. Cutting heartily for his success at bringing to Boston, alive, so interesting a specimen of Beluga Whale. It is no mean achievement to have brought it into a populous city, and have placed it in a glass tank for exhibition, even though our Whale be neither the Right Whale nor the Sperm Whale, but a smaller species."

Agassiz's letter also mentioned a welcome change at Aquarial Gardens. "When I last visited, I was particularly pleased to see the evidence of a return to a higher style of exhibitions, to say the least, and that performances previously carried on, from which nothing could be learned, have stopped!"[168]

Throughout the previous winter, the lights had often burned late in the "amusement hall" downstairs. That's what it had become. The Mammoth Ox, the Egyptian Sphinx, Arabian horses, ventriloquists and fire-swallowers were some of the acts Butler brought in. On stage, "The Robbers of Baghdad," a burlesque, ran for several weeks, replaced by "Ten Nights in a Bar Room," a moral drama. An unholy host of dancers and singers also came and went. Rumor had it that Butler ran auditions out of a backroom and, to save money, hired would-be performers with little experience, which was all too believable.

The fish ponds upstairs, and even the whale, had been reduced to a mere backdrop for the circus below.

But then, very suddenly—and this is what Agassiz was referring—Butler had left for New York, where he resumed his managerial duties at the American Museum, partnering once more with Barnum. No explanation was given for his sudden departure, but none was needed. Hallelujah! James was once more in charge of the daily operations. The staff loved him, the animals did too, and a warmth returned that was felt in every bone and fin. So did the gleam in James' eye, missing for some time.

I remember thinking, how lucky the right people occasionally end up on top!

Upstairs, James added a bottlenose dolphin to the central tank, the first exhibited anywhere in captivity. From southern waters, he brought in delicate angel fish, the first tropical fish in captivity.

Downstairs, the performances ceased, and once more the animals became the sole attraction. Their cages were cleaned; they were given luxurious amounts of fresh hay; and on certain mornings, before the public arrived, their cage doors were opened and they traipsed around visiting one another. One newspaperman hailed it as "the rarest, happiest collection of animals in the country. All sorts of animals of antagonistic nature live in harmony side by side." In short, a bit of freedom, fresh food and kindness replaced neglect and squalor.

James hung bird cages throughout the establishment, some housing large bald eagles, others home to tiny ruby-throated hummers. Still a devotee of bees, he also brought in two of his parlor hives, and people took to sitting and watching the bees make honey. In his opinion, *that* was entertainment.

Cutting's "Gardens" was back! At least for the moment. No one could have known, but the situation would reverse course yet again, all because of the person James feared the most.

Unfortunately, these were the days when newspapers printed whatever was handed them, rumors and all. A few weeks after Agassiz's complimentary letter ran, news began circulating that Phineas Barnum had transported a fine white whale down from the Gulf of St. Lawrence and was exhibiting it at his New York museum.[169] Reports described how the whale had been packed in a crate in seaweed, gingerly passed from truck, to rail, to another rail, and finally lowered into a tank at the museum. These accounts would have readers believe that Barnum's was the first whale on display, when, in reality, James was well ahead of Barnum and the mastermind behind the tricky business of transporting whales! When Barnum tried to repeat James' success, three whales died, two in transit and one in the tank. Now that he finally had a living whale to exhibit, true to form he was grabbing all the attention he could.

"Swindler!" James uttered one sticky July day. We were sitting on a bench in the Boston Common, having a late-day meal of pork pie and ale. "Barnum's a bat on my coat-tails!"

We were a stone's throw from where the Mayor had stood a few days earlier when he welcomed home the Third and Fourth regiments.[170] In those early days of the War, most of the soldiers came marching home intact. As the War dragged on, however, the returning ranks would thin considerably. The War hadn't yet impacted Aquarial Gardens' day-to-day operations too terribly, although across the river, Professor Agassiz had begun to lose staff, both at his museum and in his department, to the battlefield. Regrettably, that meant we saw him less often.

The showman's taking credit for the first exhibited whale was bad enough. Another rumor going round was that Aquarial Gardens' white whale—the true original—was on loan from Barnum. This rumor may have started because that July we had three whales in our central tank, two of which we were holding for Barnum, until his tank in New York was ready to receive them.[171] It made for a crowded situation, since the center tank also held two sturgeon, striped bass, a grey shark, turtles and more. Butler, however, hoped that James and his staff might teach Barnum a thing or two about what it took to keep captive whales alive.

That day in the park, it hit me that James, who was approaching fifty, suddenly looked old. His hair and beard had turned grayish white. His face had grown craggy, as if his deep-set eyes, long nose and mouth were caught in a rockslide.

I know he was prouder of the Aquarium than he'd ever been. He had shown the public the first shark, the first dolphin and the first whale placed in captivity, and the first tropical fish exhibited that far north. No other aquarium in the world possessed such a wide assortment of marine life. And yet James was far from a happy man. Situations arose that were beyond his control, when he wanted everything to run perfectly.

"The problem is, it never does," Professor Agassiz had tried to warn him.

As we were finishing our meal, shouts arose from across the Common, and walking over to investigate, we met up with a disturbing scene. Near the Spruce Street gate, far up in a large elm tree sat an owl. Below, a large crowd had collected. A few dozen men and boys were aiming sticks and stones at the bird, trying to topple the owl from his roost, while admirers of the bird were trying to deter them. Carriages traveling up and down Beacon Street had stopped to watch.

The owl was high enough up in the tree that most of the rocks flew passed him. But soon one struck him with such force that it knocked him off the bough. He seemed doomed to meet the ground—arms were already outstretched to grab him—when, with awakening wings, he recovered and swooped up to an even higher branch. The scene was heart-wrenching. He seemed dazed and bewildered, and made no attempt to fly off as the stoning began anew.

"Too bad there's no shooting in the park! Faster that way!" shouted one fellow. Many in the mob laughed and cheered.

A slight figure emerged from a doorway across the way and, bent low, raced into the park like a hen chasing vermin. It was Cousin Charles! He looked smaller and more pinched with scholarly myopia than ever. Yet his voice clanged authoritatively.

"Don't kill him, for God's sake!" he shouted. "If you have nothing better to do, aim at the sparrows. They're the pests. They chase our native birds, eat our buds in spring, our fruits in summer, our grains in fall."

A few years later, Charles—the Society of Natural History's curator of ethnology by then—would give a talk that famously warned of the European house sparrow's harmful presence, in America and also worldwide. The best proof that the sparrow had been an enemy of mankind for thousands of years, he said, was Egyptian hieroglyphics' use of a sparrow's image to signify 'enemy.'

"Spare this wise owl who eats mice and rats. He's a friend not a foe!" shouted Charles.

His strident outburst had an effect. The hecklers ceased their stone-throwing and dispersed. Those who remained were mainly admirers and commented to each other on the bird's large eyes and patterned feathers. Charles dashed back across the street, failing to see us, and we ourselves hurried back to The Gardens, late for afternoon chores.

Militias still held rifle practice in the Common. Otherwise, laws had prevented the average citizen from firing a gun within its perimeter since 1777. But as the papers the next morning reported, that hadn't kept someone from stealing into the Common that night and shooting the owl. "Poor bird of Wisdom," the *Boston Courier* lamented. "Its sudden popularity proved to be the death of him. As it's been said, 'The path of glory leads but to the grave.'" [172]

A thought I've carried for years is that perhaps James shot the owl. One of the bird's wings had been injured in the melee, and knowing that the owl was alone, in pain and unable to fly may have been too much for him. Maybe he resurrected the gun he had stored away. It was something James would have done, but not Charles. James' empathy toward all kinds of creatures was unusual, to the extent that he would never have chosen to kill-and-collect specimens as readily as Charles did.

You asked, when did things begin to unravel for James? I would have to say it wasn't long after the owl incident, when Henry Butler returned to Aquarial Gardens once again for reasons that were never clear. The worst part was that Phineas Barnum began turning up, too, frequently seen at Butler's side and chattering so shrilly, the animals backed into far corners when he walked by. Was it a coincidence that the more the New Yorkers involved themselves in the operations, the more The Gardens nosed downward? Not at all.

In July that summer, the dolphin died. The young boy whose job it was to feed the whales and the dolphin buckets of eels from high up on a ladder accidentally spilled iron nails from his pocket as he hung over the water. The dolphin—perhaps he mistook the shiny items on the bottom for minnows?—consumed several and died of what Professor Agassiz diagnosed as "impaired digestion."

Also in July, James' beloved seal Fanny died. She had been extremely lethargic, and one morning James found her afloat in the pool. He disappeared into his office, the sound of his sobs lasting over two hours. Fanny's brother Ned was also bereft. For several weeks he ate little and refused to perform. He was such a pathetic sight that James forgot his own sorrow in his quest to return Ned to a happier state, which he succeeded in doing.

The dolphin's demise left James without a conveyance for an act that he had poured considerable time and currency into. The plan had been to harness the ten-foot dolphin to a boat shaped like a nautilus shell, hire a pretty lady to drive it, and have them parade around the tank while the orchestra played. Agassiz was certain that the dolphin, the ocean's most intelligent creature, would carry this off beautifully. A tanner had measured the dolphin for a collar and traces, and James had hired one of Boston's most skilled shipbuilders to carve a wooden nautilus from the trunk of a giant pine tree.

In the dolphin's absence, it was Agassiz who suggested, "Vhy not the vhale?!"

When the first whale was transported from Canada, Agassiz had hovered next to the whale pond nearly every day.[173] Now, although he visited far less, he always made a beeline for the whale, fascinated as he was by its behavior. We all were! The leviathan was never still but constantly circled its glass pond, and always in the same direction. He appeared to take sport in diving up and down, and also slapping the water with his tail, as if it was his intention to elicit small yelps from anyone who got sprayed.

Once the whale's traces were made, the nautilus built, and Mademoiselle Leone hired, the pair began rehearsing. Before long, their act went public. Harnessing the whale was always tricky. When James tried to slow him down, he roared around the tank all the faster. An offering of live herring, however, got his attention, and he became a willing participant in the "cart-and-pony" show—even to the point of enjoying himself, it seemed—whereas it was Mademoiselle Leone who required careful handling. She was terrified that if she fell off the tipsy shell, the whale would devour her. Also, the whale's occasional slap of its tail drenched her hair and costume, sending her into a tizzy. The spectators were greatly amused, and clapped and cheered. They imagined the whale's shenanigans and the prima donna's prissiness were all part of the act.

Pretty is as pretty does! James was quite sure the whale's slap was deliberate.

A man on stilts strode up and down city streets shouting, "Behold exquisite Venus and the mythological Car of Venus pulled by a whale across Mimic Sea. Behold the Wonder Feat of the World!" The performance was a huge success. Nearly every show sold out, and Mademoiselle Leone became a little less petulant. For what prima donna doesn't like applause and attention?

In the spring of 1862, my employer Smyth finally was back on his feet. I was sorry to leave James, his fish palace and universe of animals, yet appreciated returning to a substantial salary and a profession that was booming, even during wartime. Drinking water! The channeling of fresh water into urban areas was a technological marvel, even though it also came with problems, from leaks to insect infestations. The introduction of Cochituate water into Boston was one of our worst nightmares, for it caused a tidal wave of cockroaches and beetles that followed water pipes into every corner of multiple buildings around the city.[174]

After I left, news from the aquarium reached me in fits and starts, and right away the tidings weren't good. With little warning, P.T. Barnum had gone and purchased The Gardens in what one newspaper described as a hostile takeover. The building closed briefly and reopened, a museum of amusements and oddities once again, with the unfortunate, luckless name of "Barnum's Aquarial Gardens." The Albino Family from Madagascar, Tom Thumb, the Mammoth Hippopotamus, the Den of Serpents. Just when you thought the most ludicrous performances possible had come and gone, more ridiculousness followed: The Living Man-Monkey, The Connecticut Giantess, the Talking Cow.

One of Barnum's publicity stunts was to have Commodore Nutt, the "smallest man alive," drive up and down Boston's narrow streets in a miniature carriage pulled by "the smallest ponies on Earth."

Once more, the aquarium itself fell into the background. Fish were perceived by Barnum as too normal to excite curiosity. Since Mademoiselle Leone was no longer the star attraction, she quit. James, the aquarium's director by title only, fell into a deep, dark depression.

The press, to its credit, was wise to Barnum's extreme measures.

"Greatness!" cried out the *Boston Advertiser*. "Some are born with it, some achieve it, and some have it thrust upon them. Prince Albert Edward was born great; Mons. Blondin has achieved greatness; while Barnum's fat boy, and all others of his acts, have had greatness thrust upon them."

James didn't last more than a few weeks working under Barnum. The day he walked out the door, he was a shattered man. Leaving Ned the seal, the beluga, the new sea lion, the Maine bears, and the rest of his beloved creatures in the care of Barnum, who was developing a reputation for exploiting animals, made him sick.[175] Before he left, he managed one small deed. He hired a wagon driver to come to the back door one evening, and they loaded a fox pair, the old tortoise, the eagles and the bear family onto the vehicle for the trip north to Maine's woods, where they were released.

Barnum never noticed their absence; nor did anyone breathe a word of the heist. In fact, one older staff member continued the ruse, periodically releasing older animals into the wild and telling Barnum they had died in their sleep.

Barnum's Gardens was sure to go bankrupt. Hadn't all of Barnum's ventures? What would happen to the rest of the animals and the fish?! Ruthless Barnum would likely send them to the New York museum. Many were sure to die in transport and the rest would suffer in deplorable conditions until death set them free.

James worked as quickly as only a desperate man can. He found another wealthy patron to partner with, and by November they had opened a new Aquarial Gardens on the corner of Summer and Chauncey Streets. He was prepared to do whatever it took to get his creatures back. But noble intentions sometimes lead nowhere. He was emotionally haggard and not as young as he once was; and he and his new business partner frequently sparred. On top of it all, he was in the throes of a patent dispute over a process for developing photographic negatives that, had it gone his way, would have left him a very wealthy man. But he lost.

When he and his business partner couldn't work things out, their aquarium, despite a flood of glowing reviews and the public's eager anticipation, closed within weeks of opening. Barnum, meanwhile, was burning through funds, and, in January 1863, his Aquarial Gardens was put up for sale. Just as James feared, its animals were shipped off to New York, Ned among them. I'm certain their departure was the last straw for James and led to his mental collapse.

How often beginnings bring happiness whereas endings bring despair. You know the tragic conclusion. James was committed to an asylum in Worchester toward the end of 1863, where he died four years later. The last time I visited him, he no longer recognized his friends and no longer spoke, his torrent of words spent. For the first time since I'd known him, his large hands lay still on his lap.[176]

Common American Swan; Cygnus americanus. John James Audubon, 1838.

PART III

The Social Light

FEBRUARY 10, 1896

In the short time it took Oliver to walk down Beacon Hill, along the dirt lanes of the Public Garden, and up the avenue to the Hemenways' stately brick house on Clarendon Street, the winter sky changed from blunt rose to the steely lavender of late afternoon. Oliver had taken the same route so many times, he knew how many trees he passed along the way. Forty-six, predominately elm and maple. This time, chased by the cold, he walked as fast as he could—he was remarkably agile for his age—taking care to skirt the icy patches that sparkled in potholes and crevices.

Near the Garden's swan pond, a figure hurried passed him in the opposite direction. It happened to be a younger cousin, Teddy Pickering, although neither man recognized the other, each was so wrapped in woolens. Historians speak of a day so cold that birds dropped from the sky. This particular day in the winter of 1896 was a close runner-up.

Harriet Hemenway, with the help of her cousin Minna Hall, was holding an informal meeting of mostly ladies that afternoon, and a few minutes after four o'clock everyone seemed to tumble through the door at once. Vigilant young maids with sturdy ankles and strong arms ran up and down the carpeted staircase, from subterranean kitchen, to vestibule, to the second-floor ballroom, to the guestrooms above, receiving and depositing wraps and passing tea and cakes with the polished efficiency the Hemenways and their maids were known for. Each time guests arrived, stepping into the warm glow of the incandescent electric lighting of the vestibule, they blinked through their tears of cold with amazement.

"Remarkable!"

"Like the sun!"

"Is it dangerous?"

The Hemenways had recently installed the Edison system, one of the first families in Boston to wire their home, and, as dusk descended, lamps on every landing were switched on for the full effect. Seen from the street, the home's interior was a warm saffron, while its neighbors looked dim and ghostly with flickering shadows.

When gas lamps first lit up Boston's streets decades earlier, Ralph Waldo Emerson had observed, "Gas-light is found to be the best nocturnal police." In this still brighter era, as illumination by means of fire receded, electric light would prove to be the best nocturnal firefighters. Raging conflagrations would start to decline.[177]

Some ninety guests were expected. Those who had accepted the invitation were entirely in agreement with Harriet and Minna's push to protect wild birds from the escalating menace of hunters and guns. However, few anticipated the path they would be led down. A great many—most, in fact—had unwittingly worn hats and muffs made of down, plumes and semiplumes, and other bird-trade claddings as protection against the cold.

There was a certain irony about the meeting time. Right at that hour, many husbands were concluding an afternoon of hunting, packing up their bird spoils and heading home. Harriet's own husband, Augustus, who was as ravenous a shot as any of his friends, was returning from Essex with a sack containing eiders and two Labrador ducks, a male and female, in his carriage trunk. He'd been amazed to come upon the pair swimming serenely in a small ice-free pond, a species not seen for years.

The greatest irony of all isn't inconceivable. On the very afternoon when his wife was launching a new Audubon society, Augustus may have been killing the last remaining Labrador ducks in North America. They fell off the face of the earth and went extinct right around that time. When exactly, no one can say for sure, but perhaps it was that afternoon at Sadie's Pond, an hour or so before sundown.

A few weeks earlier, Harriet had read an article that upset her so, she vowed to do something, anything. A fine-looking dark-haired woman with dark flashing eyes, she had a strong will to match and was ready to take her crusade to the ends of the earth if need be. The article described, in painful detail, the killing of snowy egrets in the Florida Everglades, and how plume hunters shot and skinned the older birds and left the young ones to starve.

Harriet caught her breath, devastated to realize her complicity. She had a broad-brimmed hat decorated with an egret's "long whites," its precious aigrettes. Aigrettes were referred to as "maternity plumes," because the birds acquired them while they were nesting. She suddenly saw herself as she really looked in that hat and was horrified by the image of a woman parading evidence of a murdered mother and left-for-dead baby. A murderer's accomplice!

Never again, that hat. Nor the bonnet circled with hummingbirds. Nor a fashion designer's helmet with sporty "mercury wings." She would make a large fanciful bouquet from all the feathers in her hats and replace them with dried flowers, ribbons and bows.

"How can you put something so ugly on your lovely head?" her cousin Minna had asked Harriet years ago about a blue bonnet circled with bird feathers. Harriet hadn't understood. Birds were beautiful, their feathers as decorative as flowers! But now she completely understood. Placed on the head, bird remains were anything but beautiful.

What were women thinking?

Men's thinking about guns was similarly skewed. Why should it be acceptable to slay unconscionable numbers of birds and other creatures? Why should these machines be allowed in field and forest, the inner sanctum of these delicate dwellers? The logic was upside-down, inside-out. One senseless act led to another. If birds weren't valuable enough to protect, their feathers were fine to flaunt.

Straightaway, Harriet made an unannounced visit to her cousin Minna Hall, who lived beside Swallow Pond in the same house she'd been raised in. Her family had lived there so long, the pond was also called Hall's Pond. Minna and her family always felt they had a first-row seat at the theater, the pond was so rich with wildlife.

Most people gazed upon Nature from a distance, or if they wandered into it, it was down a tidy path. Not Minna. As a quiet yet precocious girl, she had strayed off paths, waded waist-deep into ponds, slid down muddy ravines. Surprises in Nature lay around every corner. She especially became aware of this the summer she turned twelve and crisscrossed the countryside with Dr. Shattuck and the odd but amicable James Cutting as they compiled a list of Brookline birds. She asked questions neither man could answer.

What did birds say when they sang? What were feathers made of?

Exploring fields and forests made Minna supremely happy and gave rise to a fierce independence. She was confident the woods harbored neither axman nor goblin, only murmuring trees and foraging animals. As the years passed, she reconciled herself to the fact that she wouldn't make a very good wife.

In 1886, George Bird Grinnell, the editor of *Field and Stream*, launched the country's first national campaign for the protection of birds. He called it The Audubon Society, named for the naturalist, and Minna, like thousands of others, eagerly joined. "I pledge never to kill wild birds! I pledge never to wear their feathers." But Grinnell's organization was disappointingly inactive. Its members lost interest, and the organization soon ceased. Minna, however, went on patrolling active nests, feeding native birds in winter, and doing her best to convey to her friends how ugly and silly they looked with parts of dead bird on their heads.

For years to come, she made it her business to dog delinquent feather-bearers. When the Governor's wife wore bluebird feathers to the symphony, Minna sent her a contrite "think-twice-before-you-bedeck-yourself-in-feathers" note. In 1909, she would let Mrs. Taft know, graciously but firmly, that wearing feathers to President Taft's inauguration set a poor example.

When Harriet knocked on Minna's door that day, she was a changed Harriet. It doesn't take long to change. Making the decision is what takes time, and then it's usually a small leap. Suddenly, she saw things very differently. Every feather she passed on the street would make her cringe; every bird head or body would make her want to cry.

In her late thirties, Harriet had a burning desire to help the world. *Doing* over *saying* was in her and her husband's blood. Her grandfather, Amos Lawrence, and father, Amos Adams Lawrence, had seized upon manufacturing and made fortunes, her father presiding over Ipswich Mills, the country's largest maker of knit goods. Her philanthropist husband, Augustus, dispensed the income made by his father, Edward Augustus Holyoke Hemenway, who had boldly developed silver mines in South America.

When they were growing up, Harriet and her brother William had ridden to church in their grandparents' Landau, one of only two in Boston. Now William, reaping the dividends of an advantaged upbringing, was on his way to becoming Boston's renown Bishop Lawrence. Harriet hadn't been so quick to find her challenge.[178] However, when she was six, and church bells all over the city proclaimed the end of the Civil War, she had asked her parents, "Can everyone put away their guns now?" It was a sentiment she would always carry.

From a family of abolitionists, Harriet was drawn to divergent causes and individuals. When Boston's hotels refused to rent a room to Booker T. Washington, she would invite the former slave to stay with the Hemenways on Clarendon Street. She considered herself something of a rebel as well as a clairvoyant open to the paranormal. On the other hand, she was born-and-bred establishment. Hers and Augustus's families and friends supported the city's arts and culture, financial, educational and medical establishments. They supped at The Somerset Club, raced horses at The Country Club, and put on skits at The Tavern Club, the first generations to have enough money to spend it generously or frivolously—however they liked.

Because Harriet came from wealth, was married to older wealth, and was irrepressibly social, civic-minded and a touch eccentric, already at the age of thirty-eight, she was looked upon as one of Boston's grande dames. And that carried a lot of clout.

When she arrived at Minna's, she was clutching her Blue Book, Boston's bible of wealthy families and their street addresses.

"Oh, Minna, it should be a crime! Amy Pleadwell is home from Rome, and she claims so many birds have been shot around the Mediterranean, Italy is songless! And there's today's article about the plume hunters and their killing of Florida's snowy egrets! Our hats are to blame. And the milliners and their agents! But you—you've known this all along.

"I think we should send a circular to our friends asking them to join an organization that will dedicate itself to protecting wild birds—chiefly those of Massachusetts. But they must give up wearing feathers, and they aren't going to like that one bit."

Their list of names chosen from the Blue Book quickly lengthened. Their invitation held back on some details. They wanted the women to be comfortably seated in the Hemenways' chandeliered ballroom, soothed by tea and lemon cakes, before they laid it on the line. Joiners must give up their feathery finery.

Some women on their list cared far less about the bird population than they did their people fineries. Some spent a small fortune on feathers. Peggy Higgins' parasol of parrot feathers. Martha Lodge's cuff of finch. Could they be made to see the awful truth? Or would vanity prevail? Harriet and Minna weren't sure, but if they were able to win over Boston's most respected bluebloods—Mrs. Peabody, Mrs. Cabot, Mrs. Lyman, and Mrs. Elliot were essential—perhaps the rest would follow.

By the time Oliver reached #273 Clarendon Street, his toes were half-frozen, and he was glad for the Hemenways' warm foyer. The noise of women's voices coming from the upstairs ballroom sounded exactly like a great swarm of buzzing bees. Just for a moment he thought of James Cutting and his fascination with bees. And the superstitions his father and their neighbors had harbored in respect to managing them. Before hiving bees, Mr. Cutting made sure to wash the hive free of impurities with rum. The farmer and his wife tried not to argue too loudly for fear the bees might fly away. And when someone died, the bees had to be told or they might not produce.

"We've had an unfortunate loss," the elder Cutting would say within bee earshot. "Old Nestor Houghton passed away the night before, God rest his soul."

Climbing the wide staircase, Oliver was amazed by the size of the crowd inside the ballroom. The loud buzzing all but drowned out the notes of a small string quartet in one corner. All the swells were there. As were out-of-towners like Miss Jewett from the North and Mrs. Hodgkinson from the West. Oliver was one of the few men present. Off in the distance he spotted Outram Bangs, the ornithologist, and Edgar Channing, which was a surprise, since Edgar was an avid gunner and bird hunter. He'd been critical of George Grinnell's earlier Audubon group, chiding its idealistic notions and impractical goals. Edgar's viewpoint was simply "Cats kill birds, and so do humans!" He was undoubtedly opposed to the formation of this new group of "Audubonians," as he called them, and, since nothing about him had changed, save that his bird collection had grown larger, he might cause trouble.

Just as Oliver was taking in this scene, Harriet, dressed in a becoming scarlet blouse and black woolen skirt, sailed by. She pecked him on the cheek and whispered in his ear, "Thank goodness you're here. Save me from you-know-who." He knew she meant Edgar Channing. "He wasn't invited—He'll do his best to upset the apple cart, I know he will."

Oliver nodded in agreement. "No worries, leave him to me," he told her, which earned him a slightly longer peck before Harriet sailed on to other guests.

How frequently throughout his life attractive women had wrapped him around their little finger and made him say things he wasn't entirely sure he could deliver on. Two wives, now deceased, had. Two daughters and four granddaughters also were aware that he was as obliging as an old draft horse. He wasn't thrilled at the prospect of having to verbally oppose Edgar Channing or see him to the door. He had been braver in his mischievous youth than he was as a grown man. And yet, that evening he was ready to help Harriet in any way he could. He thoroughly admired her pledge to help birds and oppose those who gunned them down.

One of the maids beat on a small bongo—this was Harriet's style, always a bit bohemian—and the room fell silent. Harriet, cheerful and bright-eyed, thanked the women for venturing out on such a cold day and then briefly sallied down memory lane.

"When I was growing up in Longwood, there was a field on the opposite side of the road from our house. It was an old apple-orchard, sloping to the south, a favorite place for bluebirds. The blue of their wings will always adorn my memory! We used to search the field for nests; and it seems to me now that we found eggs of bluebirds, or robins' nests, in every tree! The boys and girls I played with all had collections of eggs, and you can be sure that far more eggs were taken from nests than added to our collections. So many broke in our clumsy fingers while attempting to blow them. Boys collected ruthlessly, but there was a resolution among the girls to only take two eggs from a robin's nest with five eggs in it. Still, no one ever left *all* the eggs. I sometimes wonder whether that lovely old orchard really did have a nest in every tree, or whether the years have distorted my memory. I can't say! Our memories of childhood are never exact. But that our attitude as children was one of ignorance and indifference to the lessening of bird life, and to the cruelty of robbing nests, is certainly true."[179]

"Minna and I asked you here this afternoon to gain your support for an organization that will build a more intelligent and kinder attitude toward bird life. It's idealistic, our plan, but what worthwhile plan isn't?"

Minna spoke next. A shortish woman, she had big watchful blue eyes and hair pulled back in a twist. She had a softer look than her cousin, but she was perfectly capable of getting down to brass tacks, as she did now. They were a good team, thought Oliver. Minna with her practical knowledge of Nature, and Harriet, less informed and yet possessing both the passion and the purse to drive the new venture forward.

"Our name—the Massachusetts Audubon Society for the Protection of Birds—borrows from Mr. Grinnell's former group. Anyone who joins must reside in Massachusetts. Our annual dues is one dollar. Because of an anonymous donor, we can afford a secretary"— everyone assumed the angel was Harriet—"and we are meanwhile indebted to The Boston Society of Natural History for temporary office space in its library."

No mystery there either, as Augustus was a trustee of that establishment. Ever since moving into its own building on Berkeley Street, the Society had increasingly gone the way of a family museum, and though funding was still a struggle, and the organization was as poor as a church mouse compared to Harvard's well-endowed Museum of Comparative Zoology across the river, the Society's new direction made sense. Older museums crammed with oddities were mostly gone. The world had caught up, distinguishing the real from the fake, and now serious content and hard science were permanently in vogue. There were lines outside the Society's doors these days.[180]

"We want to build interest in the birds of our state. A caring sensitivity. We'll strive for better laws and better enforcement. We expect each member to do her part to help protect our native birds. And also wild birds, from every region, every point of the compass. And therefore—" Minna paused. It was a beautifully-timed, effective pause. It seemed like Minna had a secret to share. Oliver, who was sitting off to one side with a view of most everyone, saw how women set down their teacups and left off eating their cakes, waiting for Minna to continue.

"And therefore, we encourage members to stop wearing the feathers of wild birds for ornamental purposes. No feathered hats; no shawls or gowns trimmed with feathers; no feathers adorning hair or wrist. You might think these items are fashionable. But what is fashionable about acquiring feathers from the cruel slaughter of birds?—so wide a slaughter, woods and fields are being stripped of one of their finest attractions."

As Harriet came forward to say a few more words, the room was so hushed that a delivery of coal could be heard rumbling down a chute across the street. It was a curiously pivotal moment that would pass as quickly as a clock's tick-tock. But it was a monumental few seconds. If Mrs. Peabody gave her table-mates a purposeful blank stare, if Mrs. Cabot heaved a long sigh, if Mrs. Lyman whispered behind a cuffed hand, if Mrs. Elliot cleared her throat, it could be curtains for the fledgling organization. Any subtle gesture might imply, 'This is a bit much, don't you think?—to be asked to give up our feathers.'

It was as if the women in the ballroom were holding their breath, waiting for a sign. But the only sign was no sign, and that was a good sign, the very best of signs.

Harriet's melodic voice rose up, and the room began breathing again. She touched on many topics. The *hundreds of millions* of birds killed throughout the world to satisfy *female vanity*. Where *masses of terns* had once thrived off Long Island, now there was *hardly a tern* to be seen! And the heath hens of Martha's Vineyard—even they were disappearing. A *sister organization* in England had formed to raise alarm over birds *lost to fashion*, and its ranks swelling. And she spoke about her friend Frank Chapman, who, while walking through Manhattan, counted nearly *200 hats* bearing the plumage and body parts of *forty species*.

"If you think a dead bird on your head makes you prettier, think again." The women twittered. "Minnie and I hope you'll take these words to heart."

We that never can make it,
Yet dare to unmake it,
Dare take it and break it and throw it away.

"We'll take questions now. And before you leave, please sign our membership book."

A gruff voice came from the back of the room. "I have a question!"

Oliver had forgotten all about Edgar Channing, and so it seems had Harriet. Her cheerfulness vanished, replaced by a pained 'do-you-really-have-to?' look.

"You profess to love birds, and you want your members to learn about their behavior. But how do you study them without shooting them? You are naïve. To know them, they must be followed in the wood, brought down, examined closely. This is why I don't protect birds, I kill them! And no apology for that. Those of us who hunt, we know birds inside and out, we know where they go, we know what they eat. And if you knew them as well as we do, you would realize that God intended—"

Edgar Channing's words were obliterated by a tremendous crash.

Oliver had earlier decided what he'd do if Edgar proved to be a nuisance. When Edgar began to speak, Oliver had stood up and strode toward the staircase, as if to leave the room, passing the delicate French Provincial table that held the tea service and trays of pies and cakes. The accident happened in an instant, his leg somehow becoming entangled with the table leg, and down he went, the table tipping to such a degree that an avalanche of Sheffield kettles, Ming china, milk, cream, ginger, lemon slices and confections rained down on him. In his youth, he and an equally mischievous cousin played tricks like this to ease the boredom of stuffy occasions, and they always got away with their prank, because the first thought anyone had was, Is everyone alright? Any broken bones? They were never scolded, only fussed over.

Now, a thousand years later, Oliver discovered he still could pull it off. The crash of falling objects was sensational, and maids came running, and women leapt up from their seats to see if he was conscious. Covered with crumbs and sugar, and his pants soaked through, he tried his best to look mortified and mildly injured.

Harriet wouldn't only forgive Oliver for the stained rug, she'd privately toast him for the rest of her life. If anyone had been watching her when the tea service came crashing down, they would have seen her expression go from anxious to quietly amused. For Oliver once had told her about his mischief-making as a youth.

The flurry of maids, the women leaping up! The bees went zigzagging in all directions, The meeting was unofficially over. Some women left. Most went to sign the register or wait their turn to ask a question. Edgar Channing was left looking left and right, no one giving him the time of day, a black crow wondering which way to fly. Before long, his tail feathers were seen exiting the front door.

When Oliver walked back across the Garden later that evening, he had on a pair of Augustus's trousers and carried his own wet pair in a bag. Although the air didn't feel that cold, he knew it was because he was warmly intoxicated and buried his nose deeper into his scarf. Harriet had made him stay to the bitter end. Minna had stayed too, and once Augustus returned, they had sipped port while doing a thorough post-mortem of the meeting. The women were flushed and excited. There had been over seventy sign-ups, nine contributions, and numerous offers to volunteer. Augustus didn't say much, tending to the fire now and then or replenishing a glass. He and Harriet had had their conversation, and he knew that in the future his hunting escapades would diminish. He didn't mind so much. He felt a bit like their cat Bordeaux, who, advancing in age, was less interested in catching birds and more content to stretch out on the terrace of their country house and watch them hop about.

Harriet's dark eyes were dancing. "Heavens knows how you pulled that off so gracefully! No broken bones. No broken china! You are positively masterful, Oliver Pickering!" Her laughter enveloped his old parched soul like a gurgling brook, and he was thankful. Women had always known how to repay him. Repayment for things that people do is never that expensive; it is just about genuine kindness.

In the Public Garden, nothing stirred. He passed the crooked little willow that he had spent endless hours climbing and swinging from as a boy. He passed the tulip bed, now winter-barren, to which, sixty some years ago, he had snuck out in the middle of the night and stolen a few dozen tulips, leaving them on the front steps of Sarah Apley's house. He hadn't been terribly proud of that raid. It really had seemed as though Mr. Teschemacher might burst a blood vessel.

A love for his departed friends, for the Earth's creatures and their beating wings, surged up expansively. His heart felt on fire. He missed his old friends; but tonight he felt their presence just above the trees. Sitting on a bench next to the pond, intending to study the night sky for only a few minutes and then be on his way, he said quite loudly, as if she was standing right there,

"Well done, Catharine! What a success! A night to remember."

And then his eyes fastened on the stars above and never let go.

Technological Advances in Boston, 1800s

1823 Gas illumination introduced, nine years after London and four years before New York; it remained the standard lighting method in Back Bay houses until 1890s

1828 First gas lamp installed in Haymarket Square by Boston Gas Co.; gas made from coal

1830 Gas lamps began to replace oil lamps on Boston streets

1834 First gas street lamp installed in Faneuil Hall neighborhood

1835 Horse-drawn omnibuses began appearing

1844 Morse's first city-to-city telegraph, which linked Washington and Baltimore

1846 First public demonstration of ether for pain-free surgery at Mass General Hospital

1846 Smithsonian Institution in Washington founded

1848 Celebration on Boston Common for water brought from Cochituate Reservoir

1849 Bostonians began using penny postage

1852 Boston was the first city in world to install fire-alarm boxes on street corners, operated by telegraph

1853 Horse-cars started to replace horse-drawn omnibus

1860s Laying of underwater Atlantic cable between America and Europe

1861 James A. Cutting's patent #31657 for aquarium aerating device was issued issued on March 12, 1861

1870 Edward Charles Pickering, Charles Pickering's nephew, then at MIT, demonstrated a telephone receiver before the American Association for the Advancement of Science, a few years ahead of Alexander Graham Bell. "In the winter of 1869-70, he gave a series of Lowell Lectures on sound, & he constructed an apparatus for the electrical transmission of sound, six years before Bell, in the same MIT laboratory, perfected the telephone. Pickering did not attempt to procure a patent. Like many other inventive physicists of the day, including Daguerre, Joseph Henry, and S.P. Langley, he held to the principle that a scientist should not place restrictions on the products of his work but share them freely."

— "Harvard Observatory" source.

1872 The Great Boston Fire

1875 Bell and Watson's first transmission of sound over wires, on Court Street, Boston

1876 Bell and Watson's first transmission of decipherable speech, 5 Exeter Place, Boston

1879 Edison's first demo of incandescent lamp, which wasn't the first electric light but well-suited for domestic use

1882 First commercial installation of electricity in Boston at Hotel Vendome; first electric street lights installed in Scollay Square

1889 Boston street lamps: 10,000 gas; 3,000 oil; 700 electric; a handful lit by naphtha; by late 1880s city-wide, gas street lamps changing to electric light, which was much brighter than gas

1889 Electrified cars taking the place of horse-drawns

1890 Oil lamps converted to naphtha gas, derivative of gasoline

1897 Boston subway completed, first in US

Acknowledgements

This book grew out of one story leading to another, most discovered in the stacks of Boston-area libraries as well as Gale's digital database of historical newspapers. For their help, I'm indebted to patient librarians at the Boston Athenaeum, Harvard University's Ernst Mayr Library of the Museum of Comparative Zoology, Harvard's Houghton Library, the Massachusetts Historical Society, and The Phillips Library at the Peabody Essex Museum. My appreciation also goes to those friends who generously read early versions of the book and gave good advice. As she has in the past, Bridget Parson Saltonstall provided infinite wisdom and editing assistance, always with cheerful encouragement (thank you!), while Stray-Bird and Zumbo have been steadfast companions through thick-and-thin.

The history of science has always fascinated me, but it was while writing about the Pickerings of Salem that I especially tumbled down a fascinating rabbit hole. So, thank you, Dickon Armstrong, for that opportunity. The Smithsonian Institution & Libraries made available numerous materials, notably the front cover's bird images and the useful account *Magnificent Voyagers; The U.S. Exploring Expedition 1838-1842* (1985). In addition, *The Forgotten Aquariums of Boston* by Jerry Ryan (3rd edition, 2011) served as an invaluable source of information about the Aquarial Gardens and the captivating inventor James Cutting.

About the Author

ANN B. PARSON is a science journalist who has written extensively about the environment, medicine, and technology. *The Birds of Dog* is her first fiction. She is the author of several nonfiction books, among them *The Proteus Effect; Stem Cells and Their Promise for Medicine*, which was selected for *Library Journal's* annual list of best science books, and *Decoding Darkness; The Search for the Genetic Causes of Alzheimer's Disease*, co-authored with neuroscientist Rudolph Tanzi of Harvard Medical School. Her published memoirs include *Antonio Ferri; Partisan Scientist*, about the revered father of supersonic flight, and *Mortimer Rogoff; Man of the Future*, about the electrical engineer and irrepressible radioman who pioneered GPS and cellphone technology. Family histories include *The House That John Built; Ten Generations of the Pickering Family in Salem*. She has written for many publications (visit www.annparson.com) and taught science journalism at the graduate level. She lives in South Dartmouth, Massachusetts.

Endnotes

Note: The book includes a few excerpts from letters and journal entries, each one identified in Endnotes. Otherwise, all stories are told in the author's own words. References found below cite the publication in which one or another story first appeared.

1 "In the spring of 1846 the geologist Josiah Whitney called Boston 'the only city in America where anything of any account is done for science.'... Despite being half the size of Philadelphia and a third of New York's population, by 1846 Boston had taken the lead in American science by possessing the deepest infrastructure to support scientific inquiry." *Henry D. Thoreau and The Moral Agency of Knowing*, by A. Tauber.

2 The Pickering house on Broad Street is considered Salem's oldest house, America's oldest home.

3 This drawing appears in *The Influence and History of The Boston Atheneum, The Atheneum Centenary*, 1907. From Wikimedia Commons. Boston's Great Fire of 1872 would reduce much of this downtown area to rubble.

4 The circus building is mentioned in *Birds of the Public Garden*, p.4, 1909. See *Memorial History of Boston*, p.614 (on-line). The Public Garden was created 1830 to 1837, from Beacon Hill landfill, and fully opened in 1839.

5 *The House That John Built*, by Ann Parson (AP). Note that in 1832 the John Pickerings moved from Franklin St. to #74-75 Beacon St., two of the six houses that had been built below Charles Street. In 1841 they moved back to their former neighborhood, to Franklin Place known as Tontine Crescent.

6 See *Atlas* editorial, Oct. 1839, for description of curassows in public garden.

7 BSNH curators were elected for special departments in 1838 for the first time.

8 Source: *The Atlas*, (Boston, MA), July 30, 1838; Issue 25.

9 N.E. Glass Company began in 1818. See "Louis Agassiz & the History of the Collection" pamphlet.

10 *Anniversary Memoirs of BSNH, 1830-80*, pp. 27 & 29. By 1839, the cabinet contained 90 of state's 120 fish.

11 It wasn't until 1837 that Massachusetts began a formal study of its natural resources.

12 Thomas Nuttall, British, was elected the Society's first president but declined because he felt a Bostonian with deep roots should preside, not a transient.

13 From Thoreau's journal: "I hate museums; there is nothing so weighs upon my spirits. They are the catacombs of nature. One green bud of spring, one willow catkins, one faint trill from a migrating sparrow would set the world on its legs again. The life that is in a single green weed is of more worth than all this death. They are dead nature collected by dead men. I know not whether I muse most at the bodies stuffed with cotton and sawdust or those stuffed with bowels and fleshy fibre outside the cases."

14 *The Rise & Fall of the Boston Society of Natural History*, by Richard I. Johnson, *Northeastern Naturalist*, Jan. 2004, Vol. 11, No. 1.

15 The earliest Chanel No. 5 is said to have used ambergris.

16 *Objects and Claims of the BSNH*, p. 4, 1861.

17 *Historical Sketch of the BSNH*, by Thomas Bouvé.

18 Ibid, p. 3. *Raleigh Register* and other newspapers, including Boston's *Daily Advertiser*, ran this story.

19 In 1831, 6 of the 7 officers at BSNH and 7 of 11 its curators were doctors of medicine.

20 *Anniversary Memoirs of BSNH, 1830-80*, p. 17.

21 *Proceedings BSNH 1875-1876*, Vol. XVIII, p. 297.

22 *Daily National Intelligencer*, Washington DC, Aug. 27, 1831.

23 Years later, before Captain Symmes's death, a then-believer, Mr. Reynolds, organized a trip to look for the southern entrance to inner Earth, but the crew was forced home due to intense wind and cold.

24 *Acquired Tastes; 200 Years of Collecting for the Boston Athenaenum*; exhibit thought to take place in 1838.

25 *The Double Elephant Folio*, by Waldemar Fries, p. 70: BSNH's purchase.

26 Parkman killed Nov. 23. 1849.

27 *The Life of John James Audubon, The Naturalist*, pp. 397-98.

28 *Bostonian Society Publications*, Vol. II, 2nd series, MCMXVII, p. 126. I believe Charles Waterton might have come up with the term "nondescript," re: assemblage of animal parts. See *Heyday of Natural History*, by Lynn Barber, about the nondescript he brought back from South America.

29 Two-headed snake. *Proceedings BSNH*, Vol. 1, 1841-44, p. 33.

30 *New-York Spectator*, Oct. 30, 1829.

31 Bostonian Society Publications, Vol. II, 2nd series, MCMXVII, p. 127. Mention of Greenwood's mermaid, though few details about its looks or origins. Barnum's autobiography, p.88.

32 References include: *The Feejee Mermaid & Other Essays*, plus article from *Brighton Gleaner*.

33 D. Webster did contribute these birds. Source: Richard Johnson's 2004 paper.

34 *Boston Journal of Natural History*, Vol. 3, 1840-41. His report presented to legislature in the session of 1838-39.

35 *Proceedings BSNH*, 1859: James Cutting made donations to the Society.

36 *Life of John Pickering*, p. 397. Originally he gave his lecture in 1833.

37 Morse & Vail gave first public demonstration of electric telegraph in Jan. 1838, in N.J. .

38 Source of several of these quotes: JP's "Lecture on Telegraphic Language," 1833.

39 Reference: "The Aquarium," *Atlantic Monthly*, 1861.

40 Source of story: *Ballou's Dollar Monthly Magazine*, Vol. 16, No.1, Boston, July 1862.

41 Source for much of material about Forsyth: *The Reverend Alexander John Forsyth and His Invention of the Percussion Lock*, by Alexander John Forsythe Reid, from information collected mostly by Mary Forsythe Reid. The University Press, Aberdeen, 1910.

42 *An Excursion Through the United States and Canada, during the Years 1822-23*, William Bane, p. 175.

43 *Boston Journal of Natural History*, Vol. 3, 1840-41, p.252.

44 *Essays on Natural History, Chiefly Ornithology*, by Charles Waterton (1838), p.162..

45 Fleet there from Nov. 23, 1838 to Jan 6, 1839.

46 Agassiz was honorary member by 1840-41, *Papers & Communication Read to BSNH*, Vol. III, p.510. According to another source, he became an honorary member Aug. 16, 1837.

47 Source of story: *The Magazine of Natural History*, July 1829, p. 218-19.

48 Direct quote from *Hunting Without A Gun* by Rowland Evans Robinson, 1905, pared down by AP.

49 One book source says there were no accounts of Daguerre's invention until March. However, AP found a reprint from the Paris Constitutional, in *Boston Courier*, Feb. 28, 1839, "Chemical & Optical Discovery."

50 Swallow Pond, also known as Hall's Pond, was near the corner of Essex and Beacon streets. (From description by Minna Hall, who lived in that neighborhood.)

51 James Cutting first lived in NH & made his beehive invention there, made money, then moved to Boston.

52 Story source: *Proceedings, BSNH,* 1840-41, p.32.

53 *Proceedings, BSNH,* 1840-41, p.47; Audubon elected to corresponding membership, BSNH, Dec. 5 1832; honorary member, Nov 3, 1841.

54 Birds of America engravings and also Audubon's *Ornithological Biography* were completed by 1839.

55 Audubon's *Ornithological Biography,* Vol 2. Note: the bird was female and just one of her "toes" got caught.

56 Quote from Audubon's chapter "The Golden Eagle," *Ornithological Biography,* Vol 2.

57 Source: *Boston Courier,* April 29, 1839. Practically the whole article revisits Morse's description of his visit with Daguerre. His letter may have first appeared in the *N. Y. Observer.*

58 *SFB Morse & the Daguerreotype,* by Sarah C. Gillespie, 2006. Contrary to Morse's letter, D's papers were not destroyed by fire. See her version of the story.

59 *Morse's Patent; Full Exposure of Dr. Chas. T. Jackson's Pretensions to the Invention,* by Amos Kendell, 1852, p. 63. Letter from *Boston Morning Post*; exact date not given, but definitely 1839 & probably @ May.

60 Details about spider appeared in Morse's Apr. 29, 1839 letter. Also, Gillespie's book, p.236.

61 See *SFB Morse & the Daguerreotype,* pp.69-70 for insights into rivalry between Morse & Daguerre.

62 Tremont Street Medical School; David Humphreys Storer was one of its founders.

63 For more about D. Humphreys Storer, see *Historical Sketch of the BSNH,* pp.77-80. Also, his profile in *Proceedings, American Academy of Arts/Sci,* 1893. Yes, he was asked to join the Exploring Expedition as a naturalist. He was a year older than Charles & likely a good friend. See BSNH essay by Richard Johnson, p.84: Storer described 90 of 120 fish in Massachusetts and every reptile. Interestingly, his son Horatio Storer became a pioneer gynecologist and is referred to as "the Father of Gynecology."

64 These examples are from John Josselyn's *Account of Two Voyages,* pp.104-15, and *New England Rarities,* p.172.

65 *Nicolas Nickleby* did take place at Tremont Theatre in June 1839.

66 Junius Brutus Booth (1796-1852) first acted in Boston in 1822.

67 Something like this did happen, although not clear when/where. Source: *Green Book Mag*, Vol.14, p.35.

68 James Cutting produced this parlor hive in later years.

69 *Historical Sketch of the BSNH.*

70 See Cabot's account about Red Owl, pp.126-27, *Boston J of NH* Vol.2 1838-39. To note, Thomas Mayo Brewer, major ornithologist, became member of BSNH in 1835.

71 Excerpt; largely CP's wording, with slight editing by AP. Sources: CP's handwritten report at Mass Historical Society (MHS), Letter #446 to Mary, and a small amount is from CP's condor passage in Cassim's book. See his report of May 22, 1839.

72 Story sources: *Observations on the Appearance of the So-Called Sea Serpent of Nahant, as seen by Himself,* Amos Binney.1839. *Civilized America*, Vol.1, by T. C. Grattan, 1859.

73 *New-England's Rarities Discovered*, footnote p.78, by John Josselyn.

74 Audubon Society, special leaflet #2, supplement to Bird-Lore, Vol.VII, no. 5, Oct. 1905.

75 *Historical Sketch*, p.44; *BSNH Proceedings*, Vol.2 (1845), p.65.

76 *The Passenger Pigeon*, by W.B. Mershon, 1907, see pp. 174-76.

77 Note distinction between passenger vs. common urban pigeon, which doesn't migrate. Yes, they would have returned to Massachusetts, mostly western Mass due to forests, in May. New England's wild pigeons were largely gone early on. Last recorded mass nesting in Massachusetts ca. 1850.

78 This news story appeared in March 1860.

79 *Log-Book of a Fisherman and Zoologist*, by F.T. Buckland, 1876. This story took place later than 1830s & 1840s. Paraphrased, and I've stretched it a bit, but not by much.

80 *The Popular Science Monthly*, Jan–June 1911; article about Draper & picture of his sister.

81 *Proceedings, BSNH*, p.7, 1841.

82 Excerpt: Mass Historical Society, Letter #450, CP to Mary. Much of letter is verbatim, with some add-ons and edits by AP.

83 *Magnificent Voyagers; The U.S. Exploring Expedition, 1838-1842*, Editors: Viola and Margolis. See p.100. Shows Mt. Kilauea drawn with camera lucida.

84 Rev. Clarke returned to Boston in 1839. Main source for this story: *Memorial and Biographical Sketches*, by James F. Clarke, Boston 1878, and his chapter "Junius Brutus Booth," p.263 on.

85 Excerpt: Booth's note largely stands. AP has made minimal edits for sake of modern-day clarity.

86 From AP's book, *A Beacon Hill Family*, p.77. Louis had been a major attraction in Germany by the 1830s; then he departed for America during or before 1840. Yes, Ludwig Rackemann played in Boston in Nov 1839 at Odeon, and again in 1840 at Melodeon. *Boston Courier*, Dec. 28, 1840.

87 After 1820, many mastodon discoveries were due to increased public awareness. Some details here relate to the Newburgh NY finding in 1845; first complete skeleton.

88 *Boston Courier*, Aug 30, 1838..

89 Metacom ruled when there was lots of exchange of Indian land for English guns, which he realized jeopardized Indians & was not a good thing. This quote made up by AP.

90 Cuvier @ 1796 referred to both lost species as "Mammoth," ten years later introducing the name "mastodon."

91 *John DuPont and Other Natural History Museum Related Murders*, by Richard Johnson, Sporadic Papers on Mollusks, I:54 (2006).

92 See *Magnificent Voyagers*, p.78.

93 *Audubon's Aviary* (2012) describes his "escalating ambivalence."

94 See Audubon's *Ornithological Biography*, Vol 3.

95 True, reported Feb. 1840, concerning rainfall in 1839 vs. 1831.

96 http://leeches-medicinalis.com/the-leeches/history/ US gov made that offer in 1835. Saw item in Boston paper around that time about someone setting up leech business in downtown Boston.

97 *History of the State of New York*, by F.S. Eastman, 1831.

98 1852, Boston was first city in the world to put fire-alarm boxes on street corners, operated by telegraph. The technology was considered a better alert system than yelling! The Great Boston Fire occurred on Nov. 9, 1872.

99 Squadron first reached Sandwiches Sept/Dec 1840; on to Pacific NW; then back to Sandwiches @ Nov '41.

100 This incident took place in Aug 1839, in Disappointment Islands. See CP's journal 2, Aug 15, 16, 26, 1839..

101 This idea actually appeared in July 1840 in a Boston newspaper.

102 *The Atlas*, Mar 6, 1838.

103 Many references for this incident include *The Great U.S. Exploring Expedition* by William Stanton and CP's journal 2, Aug. 15, 16, 17, 1839. Tepoto incident came later, Aug 23, 1839.

104 Excerpt from CP's journal (MHS), transcribed by AP. Journal 2, dates Aug 15, 16, 17, 1839. AP has edited and condensed.

105 Excerpt from CP's journal (MHS), Tahiti, Sep 23, 1839. Found & transcribed by AP. Journal book #2 or #3, pp.81-82. AP has edited slightly.

106 *Sidney Herald*, Mar. 13, 1840, reported in *Boston Courier*, July 13, 1840.

107 Both quotes from that occasion appeared in Boston papers.

108 *The Voyages of Capt. James Cook*, by James Cook, Vol 1.

109 *Proceedings, BSNH*, Vol.1, p.15.

110 Reference: *Our Own Fireside*, by Rev. Charles Bullock, 1866.

111 *Boston Courier*, Sept. 6, 1838. Note Lynn Barber's book, p.68, re: different species appearing & idea that even unicorns could be real.

112 Excerpts (with some edits by AP) from CP's journals from Hawaii visits, May 1840-Nov 1841; also Holcomb's transcript, MHS.

113 *Boston Courier*, Dec 12, 1842.

114 Sources for Waterton section: His *Essays* & also Lynn Barber's book.

115 Excerpt from CP's journal, Hawaii May 4, 1840 to Nov 28, 1841. Transcribed by R.T. Holcomb, MHS, Ms N-706. Edited by AP.

116 *I to Myself; An Annotated Selection from the Journal of Henry D. Thoreau*, 1853 journal.

117 *Narrative of the U.S. Exploring Expedition*, by Wilkes; see pp.314-318.

118 *Bostonian Society Publications*, Vol. II, 1917, p.128. Process not tried in Boston until 1841.

119 Source for many of these tales: *Birds in the Bush* by Bradford Torrey.

120 *Magnificent Voyagers*, p. 260, Jan 19, 1840.

121 Double-headed snake in BSNH cabinet, *Proceedings*, BSNH Vol. 1, p.33.

122 Barnum's autobiography: He was thinking of purchasing Scudder's by fall '41.

123 Chief references for this section: PT Barnum's autobiography (1855) and *Barnum* by M.R. Werner (1923).

124 *Old Boston Museum* Days by K. Ryan. At first Kimball's was "primarily a museum of curiosities." As audience grew, it moved to new building on Tremont between School & Court streets. First drama shown in '43. Kimball

responsible for early vaudeville! But other source (Ryan) says that theater there started right away?

125 *Proceedings, BSNH*, 1843, p.101.

126 Source: Thoreau's Journal 1: 1837-1844. This happened when he was 20, during Sept 1837. Passage shows that Thoreau really did have a sense of humor.

127 Source of story: *Greenville Mountaineer*, Greenville, SC, Apr. 23, 1830.

128 The Berkley Street building was completed in 1863 in newly filled-in Back Bay; museum's home through 1946, in which year its name changed to the Boston Museum of Science.

129 The Society received Thoreau's three principal collections after his death.

130 J.E. Teschemacher's talk at the Society's annual meeting on May 5, 1841 actually included these points.

131 Agassiz proposed his Ice Age theory in 1837; and published "Etudes sur glaciers" in 1840.

132 Dickens arrived in Boston on January 22, 1842.

133 Anning's discoveries helped provide evidence that species could go extinct. [Wikipedia:] "After her death in 1847, her unusual life story attracted increasing interest. Charles Dickens wrote of her in 1865 that "[t]he carpenter's daughter has won a name for herself, and has deserved to win it."

134 One dinosaur footprint acquired by the BSNH in 1853, belonging to dinosaurs that roamed the Connecticut Valley during the Triassic Period, was said to be the largest ever found. See Richard Johnson paper, p.84.

135 Report that Boston received one shipment of 3000 birds from Michigan, summer 1842.

136 Audubon Society, special leaflet #2, supplement to Bird-Lore, Vol. VII, no. 5, Oct. 1905.

137 Richard Johnson's paper *Rise & Fall of the BSNH*, p.84. These insects reported in 1843.

138 Notice of this fluid: *Boston Investigator*, Oct. 1839; Audubon mentioned.

139 *Proceedings, BSNH*, p.62. All true. Swans died March 1842.

140 Accounts show that Frederic played in Boston in 1842; he gave his last Boston concert in Dec. '42. See *Frederic William Rackemann, A Memoir* by his son, 1885, p.12, at MHS.

141 *Magnificent Voyagers*, p.29.

142 Third graph is excerpt from *Memoirs Read Before the BSNH*, Vol 3, "Notes on the Peeping Frog," by Mary H. Hinkley.

143 *Magnificent Voyagers*, p.230.

144 *Proceedings, BSNH,* 1859-61,Vol.VII, p. 351. Move to Mason St. took place in 1848.

145 References mention that Boston Museum illuminated into the evenings by gas, 1848.

146 Gutta-percha was first used to insulate cable @ 1849. They started making golf balls as early as 1845.

147 Source for this story: *Log-Book of a Fisherman & Zoologist,* by Frank Buckland, 1875.

148 Cutting's parlor hive was patented in mid 1840s.

149 *Boston Investigator* wrote up Cutting's invention, Sept. 12,1855.

150 *Milwaukee Daily Sentinel*, Oct. 26, 1855.

151 Tintype was hugely popular by 1860.

152 Note that Audubon used a double-barrel flintlock shotgun, possibly by 1810 or before, for shooting birds. *John James Audubon*, by Richard Rhodes, p.74.

153 This London aquarium opened in 1853 at the London Zoo, the latter founded in 1828. Note that some refer to it as the first "public aquarium." However, it operated as part of the zoo.

154 Cutting had developed two perfect fish tanks as early as 1854. See Henry Butler's *The Family Aquarium*, about reciprocal exchange between plants & fish.

155 April 1859.

156 Club started in 1854; see *New England Mag,*Vol. 19, online.

157 *Charles Darwin's Diary of the Voyage of HMS Beagle*, preface.

158 References for much of aquarium's early era: *The Forgotten Aquariums of Boston*, by Jerry Ryan, Third Edition 2011 and *Ballou's Dollar Monthly Magazine,* July 1862.

159 *Ballou's* July 1862 article. Opened with tanks using vegetation, but switched to aerating the water with Cutting's invention.

160 *Life, Letters, and Works of Louis Agassiz*, by Jules Marcou.

161 *The Forgotten Aquariums*, p. 27.

162 *Boston Daily Advertiser*, Mar 15, 1861. This was in Agassiz's 1860 report.

163 Reference for details about this system: *Ballou's* July 1862 article.

164 *The Family Aquarium; Aqua Vivarium*, by Henry D. Butler, 1858.

165 Tetu received patent in 1853; see online info.

166 *Ballou's* 1862 article.

167 These dimensions of whale from Cutting's letter in *Ballou's*.

168 *The Forgotten Aquariums*, p.38. Agassiz's letter ran in the *Boston Journal*, May 27, 1861.

169 Ibid., Barnum's trying to take credit, pp.37-38.

170 *Boston Common; Scenes from Four Centuries*, p.69, July 23, 1861.

171 *The Forgotten Aquariums*. Three whales in central tank in July 1861.

172 *Birds in the Bush*, by Bradford Torrey, pp.29-30. This owl story happened later in century, but it happened.

173 I read (in "Ocean Wonders"?) that Agassiz came by every day.

174 *Boston Daily Advertiser* reported on this, Sept. 1862.

175 Henry Bergh, who started ASPCA, criticized Barnum, who eventually started an ASPCA chapter.

176 James Cutting's *New York Times* obit: August 1867.

177 Big change from gas to electric street light by 1880s—much brighter.

178 William Lawrence served as the 7th Bishop of the Episcopal Diocese of Massachusetts, 1893-1927.

179 This paragraph is excerpted from *Sixty Years Ago*, by H.L.H., Bulletin of Mass Audubon Society, 1926. In her own words, although edited and pared down by AP.

180 The BSNH changed its name to the New England Museum of Natural History (1940s). It was then renamed the Boston Museum of Science in 1951 and moved to its present location.